The
World
of
CB Radio

The original **Big Dummy's Guide to C.B. Radio** has received international acclaim as *the handbook* on CB radio. Due to popular demand, this new global edition—**The World of C.B. Radio**—was expressly produced to keep up with the latest developments in today's CB World.

The Authors

The World of CB Radio

by
Mark Long
Albert Houston
&
Jeffrey Keating

The Book Publishing Company **Summertown, TN USA**

THIRD EDITION
FIRST PRINTING----1987

Library of Congress Cataloging-in-Publication Data

Long, Mark
   The world of CB radio.

Rev. ed. of : Big dummy's guide to C.B. radio. 1st ed. 1981
Includes index
1. Citizens band radio   I. Houston, Albert.   II. Keating, Jeffrey.   III. Long,
Mark. Big dummy's guide to C.B. radio.   IV. Title.
TK6570.C5L66   1987   621.3845 4   87-70878

ISBN: 0-913990-53-1

Portions of this book originally appeared as:

The Big Dummy's Guide to CB Radio and
The Big Dummy's Guide to British CB Radio

Executive Editor: Mark Long
Cover Artist: Peter Hoyt

Printed in the United States of America
by R.R. Donnelley & Sons

Table of Contents

Acknowledgments

We would like to thank the following individuals for their contributions to the original **Big Dummy's Guide to CB Radio:** William Brady, William Hershfield, Peter Hoyt, David Long, Paul Mandelstein, Matthew McClure, Bruce Moore, and Mark Schlicting. We would also like to thank the following individuals for their contributions to the original **Big Dummy's Guide to British CB Radio:** Disco One, James Hartman, Gordon Henderson, Gregory Lowry, and Arthur Saarinen. All contributed their expertise and time in one way or another.

The following companies also contributed photos and information on their respective radio products for this edition: Icom America, Midland International Corporation, Opto-electronics Inc., Tandy Corporation, and the Uniden Corporation.

Finally, but certainly not last, the following individuals were instrumental in producing this global edition of the **World of CB Radio.** Peter Hoyt designed the cover and redrew some of his original technical drawings from the earlier editions. Kathleen Long proof-read the manuscript, computerized a mountain of information and assisted in the contact of contributors to this work. Our thanks to Peter, Kathleen and all the other Big Dummies whose help made this book possible—all former members of the KHT 1296 group.

Mark Long
Albert Houston
Jeffrey Keating
April 1987

The
World
of
CB Radio

Introduction

There's all kinds of folks getting into CB radio nowadays. CB radio has really become the people's radio service. It offers free communications for anyone who wants it, and you don't have to know a lot of fancy radio theory to get on the air. You can even get CBs factory equipped in some new automobiles. So you might have ended up with a rig and not know much about how to use it or how it works. Or maybe you're interested in getting a CB but don't know where to start. In the first few chapters we discuss buying a rig, getting it set up to work, and talking on it. Also we'll give you some simple explanations about how they work. If you're an old time CBer and have had a rig for awhile, there are some interesting ideas a little later in the book.

CB communication is not only fun—it's also smart. On the super highways, back home or in the office, CB is a useful tool for almost everyone. Truck drivers, motorists, and the highway patrol all use CB radios to keep things together on the road. It gives them an extra sense that stretches them on out miles ahead on the interstates and highways, so that they can perceive changing road conditions, weather, accidents and other driving hazards. Truck drivers use CB as a means of staying intelligent behind the fast-paced, hammer-down lifelines of North America and Europe.

Owning a CB radio will also let you talk to your home from your mobile via the radio airways. It's convenient for saving time at stops, sending instructions, and relaying important phone calls and messages, as well as for helping you stay connected to your family. A CB radio also can offer a means of staying connected with your business. For many people, the added communications means added gain as well. CB communications add an extra means of being in the right place at the right time.

In an emergency, CB radio may be the only means of getting help. There are emergency groups (HELP and REACT in the US; THAMES and HARP in the UK and Ireland) that monitor the radio and can offer help and assistance. These folks also help in times of natural disaster. Many police vehicles are now equipped with CB's too, making them more readily available to motorists when needed.

CB clubs around the world have been instrumental in getting CB recognized as an excellent radio service for the public. Legalization in Europe, for example, has come about because of dedicated efforts by groups such as these. They offer you the opportunity to get to know your fellow breakers off the air as well as on it. CB clubs have also joined together to offer assistance to folks in need of help, often giving aid to the elderly and the disabled. You can check around and find out where the local CB club meets in your area. We discovered that there are a lot of good folks out there to meet!

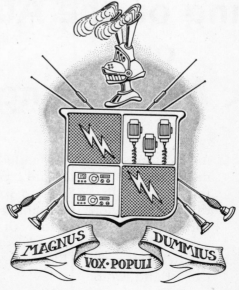

Chapter One

Getting on the Air
or
Basic Modulating

A CB radio is technically called a transceiver, which is a combination of a transmitter and receiver. Your car radio is a receiver that you can listen to—but you can't talk back to the DJ. CB radio can be more fun than a regular radio, because you get to communicate with the folks that you hear. Throughout the book we use CB, CB radio, rig, transmitter, hunk of junk, chicken box, squawk box, and the like, interchangeably with the words "Citizens Band radio."

Well, you can't actually hear the radio waves themselves. Your voice is hooked onto the radio waves by a process called modulation. Modulating also means talking on your CB. We use modulate, modjitate, and ratchet jawing to mean the same thing. When you first get a rig you could give a listen for a while to get the feel for what's going on. If you want to jump right in there, though, don't worry—the other folks on the channel will let you know how you're doing. CB is a down-home mode of communication and folks will love modulating with you. If you don't understand all the lingo, check out our international directory of Channel Jive at the end of the book.

Breaking the Channel

There are forty channels for use, and each one may have as many as hundreds of users in certain areas. With so many folks using CB, you need to make sure that the channel is not in use before bulldozing your way in. The most common way to do that is to "break the channel". Always listen to see if someone is talking. Then you can say, "Break one-four," (if you're on channel 14), and usually if the channel is free, someone will come back and say, "Go breaker," or you might be asked to "Stand by" or "Hold on." If you don't hear anything, you can assume that the channel is clear and make your call. Other things you might hear for breaking the channel are "break, break," "breakity-break,"or "breaker broke break," etc. Asking for and giving a break keeps the channels from drifting into total madness.

Turn that radio on. Take a spin around the dial. Listen to some of the people talking. Keep in mind that you are entering another dimension, and it would be wise to learn the ways of the people that you will be talking to. A few minutes of turning the channel selector should inform you which channels are in local use.

If a channel is already in use, and you would like to join the conversation, wait for one of the stations to finish a transmission and then quickly press your mike and say,"station on the side!" One of the breakers on the channel might let you in by saying, "station on the side, go ahead."

Getting a Handle

Your handle is your CB alternate personality code name. You might only get to know the folks that you meet on the CB by their handles.

One way to get a handle is to have your friends think one up for you, or you might think up one on your own. You may go through a few, but eventually one will stick.

Radio Check

One of the first things you'll want to do with your rig is to get a "radio check." This is when you call out on the channel for the purpose of finding out how well your radio is performing. A typical radio check might go like this:

Break for a radio check.

Go ahead, radio check.

10-4. You got the Big Dummy. Who we got there?

You got the Fox. You're comin' in good here—putting about nine pounds on my meter. And good modulation, c'mon.

10-4, guy. We appreciate the check. We'll back 'em on out. The Big Dummy, going breaker break!

Folks can give you information in a radio check in two ways. They can listen to you and tell how it sounds to them. If you are kind of weak they might say that they "got you back in there." A signal might get a "definitely making the trip." Strong signals can get you a "wall-to-wall" report or "you're bending my windows." Another way to give a radio check is by using the S-meter (signal strength meter). Many radios have an S-meter on them. Stations that you talk to will move your S-meter to varying degrees, depending on the strength of their signal and their location. "You're putting about nine pounds on my meter," means his S-meter is reading 9 when you're talking. For higher readings like 20 or 40 or so, folks sometimes say, "You're pegging my meter," or "You're in the red." Ways to describe how you are getting out are as countless as the sands of the Ganges River.

S-Meter Reports

Got you way back
in there. (S - 1)

You're a bit 10–1
on me, c'mon. (S - 3)

Good copy—
nice one. (S - 6)

Wall to wall and
tree top tall. (S - 9)

Busting my
speaker. (S - +20)

Blowing out my windows.
(S+ & a broken meter)

Frequencies: The 27 MegaHertz Citizen's Band

By international agreement, many countries have allocated radio frequencies in the 27 MHz range for use by their respective national CB radio services. When talking about a radio frequency on the 27 MHz CB band, we mean a regular wave with a frequency of 27 million cycles per second. That means 27 million waves, each 11 meters long, radiate from your antenna each second, traveling at the speed of light!

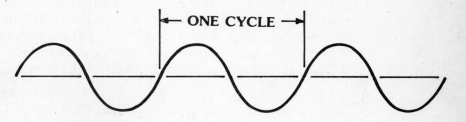

Fig. 1-1 One cycle

One cycle per second is also called a Hertz, named after the early radio pioneer, Heinrich Hertz, who first experimented with radio waves back in the late 1800's. One thousand cycles per second is also called a kiloHertz (kHz), and one million, a Mega-Hertz (MHz). Twenty-seven million cycles per second = 27 MHz.

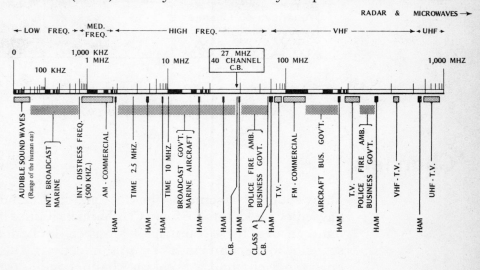

Fig. 1-2 Radio frequency spectrum

AM/SSB vs FM CB Radios

When talking into your CB mike, you are hitching your voice to a radio wave. AM (Amplitude Modulation) and FM (Frequency Modulation) are two modulation methods used to accomplish this. In the US, Canada, and elsewhere in the Americas, AM is the most commonly used modulation method, although a derivative of AM known as SSB (for Single Side Band) is also legally available. SSB is a stronger, more compact form of AM, and it is very popular among those CBers who like to communicate over extremely long distances. Even locally, a SSB signal has 1½ to 2 times the range of an AM or FM signal of equivalent power. For every AM channel, there are two SSB channels: an Upper Side Band (USB) and a Lower Side Band (LSB).

FM CBs are legally allowed in the United Kingdom, Ireland and elsewhere in western Europe. Like the US, the UK has authorized forty channels for use, with a maximum of 4 watts output power to the transmitter section. The UK FM channel frequencies are on slightly higher 27-MHz frequencies, however, than those used in the United States and Canada.

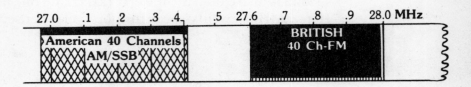

Fig. 1-3 American vs. British Channels

Channels

Many countries (including the US, Canada, Ireland and the UK) have allocated a total of forty CB channels for use in the 27 MHz band. In all of these countries, a few specific channels have been set aside for certain kinds of communications. These include an emergency channel, a breaking channel, and a traveler's channel.

Emergency Channel. Channel 9 is used only for communications involving an immediate or potential emergency situation. It is recommended that you keep the channels on either side of the emergency channel clear, to prevent causing interference to the emergency channel.

Breaking Channel. Each town or local community has one or more channels where CBers can listen or call for their friends. When using a breaking channel it is important to move to another channel as soon as possible, so that the breaking channel remains free for others to use. You can ask around and find out which channel is used for breaking in your community.

Break, one-four

Go, breaker!

Hey, we thank you for the break. How about it Big Dummy? Are you on this Smokeytown channel, get back?

Four sure! Who do we got on that end? C'mon.

You would have the Lucky Lady here. Let's clear this breaking channel and kick it up to two-three for a ratchet, c'mon.

Roger Dee. We gone to 23.

Traveler's Channel. Channel 19 is the traveler's channel It's used by people on the road to communicate about what's happening. The truckers keep in touch as to traffic and highway conditions, accidents or hazards. They also use it for directions and as sort of a Yellow Pages to find out a good place to eat or when to park their semi for the night.

Also truckers use the Channel 19 to keep track of Smokey the Bear. It is very important to leave Channel 19 for the truckers and other mobiles that are traveling on the interstates, motorways and highways. With forty channels available for everyone's use, it is only fair to give travelers a break and keep 19 clear for their use. A Channel 19 conversation on the superslab in England might go something like this:

Break one-nine for a copy!

Go ahead breaker we got a copy.

You got the Daredevil on this end.. What's yer handle, guy?

You got the One-Eyed Jack. What kind of wheels are you pushing c'mon?

We're pushing big wheels and we got the hammer down for Spaghetti Town, is that a four?

Aye, that's a four. We be southbound for Smokeytown. You be careful round that Spaghetti Junction. There was a Jam Sandwich collecting green shield stamps when we passed through, fetch it back!

That's a four, Jack. Appreciate the info. It's looking clean and green back towards the Smoke. So we'll give you the high numbers. Keep it clean and don't be seen. May the blue light never shine upon you. You got the Daredevil northbound and down!

Four fer sure, Daredevil. 10-10 till we do it again. We up, we down, we gone, bye bye!

Ten Calls

> **How about it Big Dummy? Are you 10-8, break?**
>
> *10-4. Bring it on dude!*
>
> **What's yer 10-20 now Big Dummy?**
>
> *We just passed 14th avenue on the south side, c'mon.*
>
> **You were a bit 10-1 on me that time, so give me a 10-9 on that, kick it back.**
>
> *I said that we just passed 14th avenue on the south side, c'mon.*
>
> **That's a big 10-4. We're 10-10 and listening in.**

Those CBers were saying "10-4" and "10-8." They are using ten signals, which are agreed upon radio shorthand that folks use throughout the world. In some cases the 10 part of the number has been dropped as in saying "give me a nine" instead of asking for a 10-9. The calls go from 10-1 to 10-100. Here are some of the more commonly used ten signals.

10-1	Weak copy	10-20	Location, also rough location
10-2	Loud and clear		
10-3	Stand by	10-27	Moving to Channel ___
10-4	Yes, Okay, Roger	10-30	Illegal use of radio
10-5	Relay, Repeat information for another station	10-33	Emergency traffic on the channel
10-6	Busy at present	10-34	Request for assistance
10-7	Out of service, Off the air	10-36	Correct time
10-8	In service, On the air	10-46	Assist motorist
10-9	Repeat	10-77	Negative contact
10-10	Standing by	10-100	WC or restroom stop
10-13	Weather and road conditions		

If you hear a 10-33 on any channel, that means there is emergency traffic happening on that channel. Try to help out. This may mean just being quiet.

Also there is another expression, "Code Three," which is used when talking about emergency vehicles, using lights and siren. "There's an ambulance southbound running code three!!"

Squelching The Noise

Between conversations on your radio you will hear a lot of noise and static. The squelch knob on your radio can be set to turn off this noise and yet let you pick up any breakers. Here's how to set it:

While listening to the background noise coming out of the radio's speaker, adjust the squelch knob clockwise slowly until the background noise just disappears. Leave the control at this setting. The receiver will remain quiet now until someone transmits a signal on your channel. That signal will "break" the squelch and be heard by you. Remember, it is important not to turn the squelch control too far beyond the noise cut-off point, or some of the weaker stations on the channel will not break through it. When trying to copy a weak station with your AM CB radio you may want to leave the squelch off so that you can hear anything that takes place on the channel.

On FM if a station isn't strong enough to break the squelch, it won't be strong enough for you to understand clearly anyway. So don't feel that you have to listen to that old receiver hiss in order not to miss anything, because you don't. If you do, after a while the noise will drive you crackers!

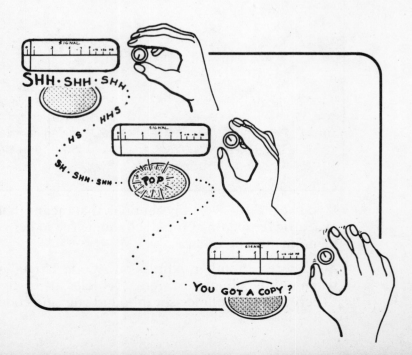

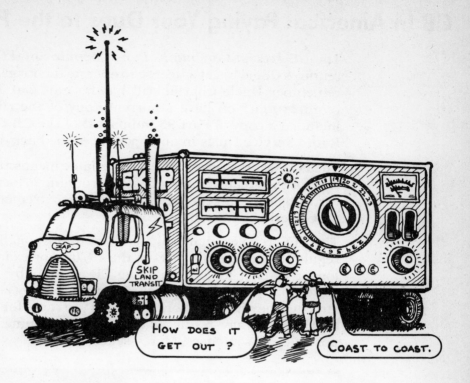

Skipland

On some days, you might hear people talking from far away places not within the usual range of your radio. You can receive these long-distance stations because the radio waves are bouncing off the ionosphere, the high atmosphere around the earth. The sun causes layers in the ionosphere to become electrically charged and act like a mirror for the radio. At certain times, the radio waves can be reflected back to earth, skipped great distances with leaps and bounds. That's why we call it the "skip."

Stations talking skip use unusual names and numbers. They are also probably using gigantic antennas and high-powered transmitters. If you try to talk back to them from your weak little mobile, they might not hear you. Don't be alarmed. Legally, you're not supposed to talk that far anyway. It may be hard to find a clear channel in times of heavy skip. Just wait a while, and the skip will roll out just like it came in. Usually there is no skip at night.

CB In America: Paying Your Dues to the FCC

The US *Federal Communications Commission* (FCC) no longer requires CBers to get a license to operate their rigs, by golly. But remember Uncle Charlie still has his ears on! The FCC also requires that you have a current copy of the rules. We have included a copy of **Part 95 Subpart D of the CB Citizens Band Radio Service Rules** in an appendix in the back of this book.

The FCC wants to keep CB a good reliable means of communication for the greatest number of folks running in local areas. They frown on skip talkers and folks running extremely high power that interfere with other people.

The FCC relaxed many of its more mind boggling rules and regulations concerning CB in the 1970s. For example, they no longer restrict folks from using CB as a hobby. On the other hand, they plan to enforce the regulations they still have more strictly. They have authority to issue warrants for illegal operation, which may result in the loss of equipment, fines, and possible jail sentences. Mercy sakes!

So get a load of the following FCC rules and regulations:

Remember that Channel 9 is reserved for emergency traffic. At all times you must give priority to emergency communications.

You must use an *FCC Type Approved* CB transmitter as your CB station.

The use of a linear amplifier (kicker) on the CB bands is not legal, and having a linear amplifier present (i.e. under your seat) can be considered "de facto" evidence of its use.

If you are causing television interference, you are required to install a "low pass filter" on your rig.

Don't use obscene or profane language on the air.

You should not in any way intentionally interfere with the communications of other stations. Nor can you deliberately transmit off frequency (a feat which requires tampering with your rig).

The use of CB for broadcasting or the reproduction of music is prohibited.

Your communication with another station should be limited to the minimum amount of time practical. In other words don't hog the channel.

Never transmit the word May-Day or any other international distress signal unless there's is a confirmed *grave and imminent danger to life or property.*

If we remember how many fellow CBers there are, and that we're all in this together, everything will be all right! 10-4!

CB in the United Kingdom:
Paying Your Dues to the Home Office

In the United Kingdom, the Home Office—Radio Regulatory Department, is in charge of administering the airwaves. In Great Britain, portions of the 27 MHz and 934 MHz bands have been allocated for the Citizen's Band Radio Service. A copy of the Home Office Radio Regulatory Department performance specifications for CB radio is included in an appendix in the back of this book. The most important points are summarized below:

The operation, importation and installation of unapproved CB radio equipment is illegal under the Wireless Telegraphy Act of 1949 and 1968. Violators of this act are liable for possible jail sentences, fines and confiscation of illegal equipment!

The British government issues licenses. Each owner is given a call sign after filling out an application and paying a license fee. The Post Office Radio Interference Service (a division of the GPO), has set certain technical standards to ensure both the effectiveness of CB and the minimum amount of interference to other radio services. All stations are required by law to use only *type approved* radios that are manufactured for 27 or 934 MHz FM. All previously imported AM/SSB radios remain illegal for use in the UK. It is the responsibility of the owner to ensure that only type approved radios are used. All type approved equipment will have a 27/81 circle stamped or engraved on the radio's front panel.

CB 27/81

The new license makes you responsible for whatever happens on your rig. Not everyone in your family will need to get a license— one license covers it all. If you have a business, one license can cover your employees as well. No exam is required.

The Home Office wants to keep Citizen's Band a good reliable means of local communications; it is their position that if people want to communicate over long distance and make international contacts, they should become licensed radio amateurs by taking the amateur radio exam. DX contacts on CB are considered an illegal offense.

All British 27 MHz CB antennas are limited to a single element rod or wire antenna with a length of 1.5 meters (59") or less. This effectively limits the range of local as well as DX communications. All other antennas used by CBers on the continent and in the US are illegal for use on British CB channels. Antenna height is also restricted to below 7 meters (23 feet) unless a power reducer or attenuator is used to limit the transmitted signal to less than one-tenth of its unattenuated amount. This would take your 4 watt signal down to toy power levels of less than ½ watt. All type approved CB radios are required to have a switch or other means of easily accomplishing this.

The Home Office decided to put its 27 MHz CB service on frequencies located above the regular American AM/SSB channels. They felt that by doing this, a more reliable service would be possible, eliminating much of the interference caused by skip and the illegal local operation of AM/SSB equipment. It is just about the only legal 27 MHz CB service in the world operating on those frequencies!

A license from the Home Office, Radio Regulatory Division, is required for any CB radio equipment capable of transmitting. This license will need to be renewed periodically.

All CBers are required by law to purchase and use only CB transmitting equipment that has been type approved for use within the UK.

You are expected to say your assigned identification numbers at the beginning and end of each transmission. Handles are not a bona fide substitute for your call numbers.

Never transmit the word May-Day or any other international distress signal unless there is a confirmed grave and imminent danger to life or property.

You should not in any way intentionally interfere with the communication of other stations.

Keep transmissions brief and to the point.

The use of CB radio for anti-social purposes is prohibited.

Do not use obscene or profane language on the air.

The use of CB for broadcasting or the reproduction of music is prohibited.

British 934 MegaHertz CB Rigs

The UK Home Office has also licensed CB communications by means of a second, higher-frequency portion of the radio spectrum around 934 MHz. While 27 MHz is considered a High Frequency (HF) Band, 934 MHz is called an Ultra High Frequency (UHF) Band.

On UHF frequencies, all skip interference is eliminated. Radio waves on 934 MHz are too short to skip off the ionosphere (they just kind of slip through it). 934 MHz radios have twenty channels for use, and eight watts of input power is the maximum allowed. The higher power helps to offset some of the disadvantages of UHF. Unlike HF radio waves, which can travel along the ground, around buildings and over hills, UHF communications are strictly limited to line sight. All UHF antennas must be located at high and clear elevations for good results.

UHF radios are the product of a new and sophisticated communications technology and their cost is several times that of the more common 27 MHz radio. The higher cost of this equipment means less crowded channels and is suited to certain business applications, where more private means of communication is desired. Because the 27 MHz FM equipment is alot cheaper than the 934 MHz gear, most of Britain's new CBers are now using the lower frequency band. Consequently, it is a lot easier to get a comeback when using the breaking, road or emergency channels on 27 MHz.

Fig. 1-4 Uniden UHF CB
(Courtesy Uniden)

UHF radios operate on frequencies similar to those used by microwave ovens. There is still some question as to the long term health effects from the user's exposure to microwave radiation. The National Radiological Protection Board advises against placing your hand closer than 10 centimeters to a transmitting 934 MHz antenna or damage to your eyes may result. All 934 MHz walkie-talkies are limited to 3 watts or less as a precautionary measure.

Chapter Two

Buying a New Rig

CB radios can be constructed in many different ways and come with lots of "extras." These extras, most of which are used for listening, make the difference in the price of most radios. The many combinations of these features makes for a lot of different CB radios on the market. Now it doesn't matter if you are driving a Yugo or a Porsche, you can still get around. And with a moderate expense you can get into the CB action. In fact, the reason that we call these features "extras" is because they are extra and not necessary to get out well.

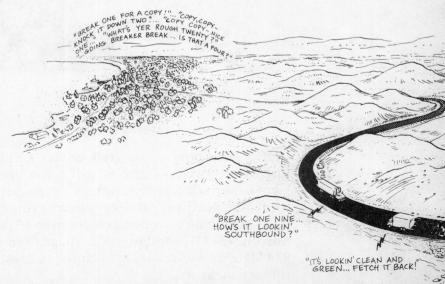

"BREAK ONE FOR A COPY !"... "COPY, COPY, KNOCK IT DOWN TWO"... "COPY COPY NICE ONE"... "WHAT'S YER ROUGH TWENTY ?"... "GOING BREAKER BREAK ... IS THAT A FOUR ?"

"BREAK ONE NINE... HOW'S IT LOOKIN' SOUTHBOUND ?"

"IT'S LOOKIN' CLEAN AND GREEN... FETCH IT BACK!"

Legally, you aren't supposed to improve the transmitting quality by boosting the power. So manufacturers try to improve the performance of their units in other ways, by adding extra circuits that let you pull in weak stations or cut down on noise and interference. While some of these features do help, they are not critical. Don't get snowed into thinking you need a crystal lattice filter or a range expander in order to get out, because it isn't true.

A *transmitter* is the generator of your radio signal, but it's the antenna that both catapults your signal outward on transmit, and captures the signals on receive. So keep in mind that you are going to need a **good antenna** and coaxial cable. This is one of the most important factors in how well your radio is going to get out.

The power that your radio will put out affects its performance and its price. The power used by your CB is expressed in two ways: as power input and power output. The power input is the amount of power used by the transmitter to produce what goes out. The power output is the amount of power which actually gets out of the radio. Power is measured in watts. Both the U.S. Federal Communications Commission and the British Home Office have limited the output power of CB radios to 4 watts, which is what most new American and British CB rigs deliver. So that's the best you can legally do. The amount of power you

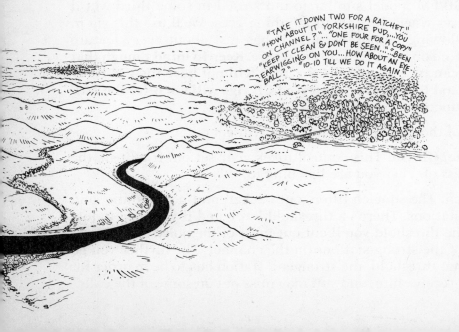

put out affects your range of communications. Four watts output power to the antenna can provide relatively good communication in a radius of 10 to 20 miles or more. Limiting communications to low power was designed to improve quality of local CB communication by cutting down interference from the traffic of neighboring communities. It also allows there to be many folks on the air at once.

Now maybe you aren't too concerned about getting out the maximum distance possible. There are cheaper rigs with fewer watts. The most common kind is the walkie-talkie. Some walkie-talkie models put out less than one watt of power. The lower power of these units combines with the smaller antenna size and lower antenna height to keep them from getting out as well as other rigs. A stronger rig will help talk around hills and buildings, and will cut through the interference better, so it never hurts to have more watts. It is usually worth the added expense to have the most power out that you can get.

Knobs and Dials

Let's take a gander at the ultimate CB radio. It has all kinds of fancy knobs and dials and switches on it, and you might be wondering what they are for. Here is a list of common ones and what they do. The rig shown on the next page is an international AM/SSB/FM model similar to units used in some third-world countries where just about anything goes. We'll use this rig in the following section because it has just about every feature you'd find on any CB radio anywhere. **Keep in mind though that American type-accepted CB radios will not have the FM functions, and British type-approved CB rigs will not offer the AM/ SSB functions.**

None of these affect how well you will get out.

Volume, Off/On. This control turns your set on. It adjusts the loudness of what you are listening to.

Squelch. The squelch filters out background noise, static, and weak stations. There's a threshold level, and if you turn to just pass the threshold you'll cut out most of the noise but still get most of the strong stations on the channel. The further you go past that threshold, the stronger a station has to be in order for you to receive him, and you may miss out on some of the calls.

Channel Selector. This knob selects which of the possible 40 channels you are transceiving on. Push button control and lighted readout have become popular. Some radios have push button control scanners that will keep moving from channel to channel with one button held down. For convenience, some companies are putting the channel selector in the mike, a repairman's nightmare.

Automatic Noise Limiter and Noise Blanker (ANL & NB). These switches cut down on static and ignition and motor noise. They help filter out noise interference to keep it from getting into your receiver and making it harder for you to hear.

Delta Tune. The delta tune is a control provided for on some transceivers which make it possible for you to tune in stations that are a little off the center of a channel. Try different settings of this while listening to the station you want to hear.

RF Gain Knob. When used properly, this one cuts down the RF (radio frequency) volume in your receiver amplifier. It can be adjusted to cut down noise on nearby stations. It has a knob which gives you lots of possible settings. Run with the RF gain up all the way unless you get close to a station and it starts sounding so loud that it distorts your receiver.

Fig. 2-1 Uniden European CB PC-404 (Courtesy Uniden)

Distant-Local. This switch is an attenuator that in the local position prevents local up-close CB radio traffic from overdriving an AM receiver. The distant position is the normal one which gives you the full range and sensitivity of your receiver.

Meter. Most meters have two scales—one for transmitting and one for receiving. One lets you know how strong a signal you are putting out and the other lets you know how strong a signal you are picking up. The first one is a relative power out meter. The second is a signal strength meter (S-meter).

Mode Switch. Some of the higher-priced American CB radios offer the operator the option of selecting between AM and SSB modes of operation. Additionally, a few of the CB radios used in third-world countries have been manufactured to allow the operator to switch between AM, SSB, or FM modes. In all cases, multi-mode CBs can transmit as well as receive the selected mode.

Clarifier. This control is used on SSB CB's only. Unlike AM or FM

Fig. 2-2 Midland 77-149 mobile CB radio (Courtesy Midland Int'l)

receivers, which are locked onto the channel frequency, the SSB receiver must be fine tuned for best reception. This control normally does not change the transmitted frequency.

LED Digital Readout. This display gives the channel number a lighted digital readout.

Hi/Low Tone Switch. This control acts like a sound filter on your receiver. It is similar to a bass/treble control on a stereo, and it allows you to select the sound that you like best.

Hi/Low Channels. While this kind of feature is illegal in the US, Great Britain and elsewhere, some of the CB radios manufactured for use within third-world countries have this switch on them. This provides foreign CB operators with a way to move to quieter frequencies whenever skip from US CB stations starts rolling into their neck of the woods. When placed in the low position, the radio operates on the regular 40 AM channels. When placed in the high channel position, the radio will operate on 40 more channels that are located above the regular AM 40 channels. In many cases the LED Digital Channel Readout will then count from channel 41 to channel 80.

Channel 9 Switch. This control allows you to switch instantly from any channel to the channel 9 emergency frequency. When this switch is engaged, the regular channel selector is inoperable.

Channel 9 Priority. When this is switched on, your receiver automatically listens every second or two on channel 9, and if anyone is transmitting there, the receiver stays on 9 until they're done transmitting. Usually the squelch must be set properly for this to work. This feature is usually only used by channel 9 emergency monitoring operators, and it must be switched off for normal operation.

Fig. 2-3 Uniden Pro-540-E CB (Courtesy Uniden)

Sending

All of these do affect how well you will get out.

Microphone. The push-to-talk button is on the mike. You have to push it to transmit and let go of it to receive. You can't hear anybody if you're holding that button in! But they will hear you if you talk clearly and at an even tone close to the front of the mike. A *Power Mike* is a special microphone for AM/SSB rigs that has a built-in amplifier. It is usually sold as a separate item. Most new radios have ample modulation with the microphones that they come with, but a power mike can help out most any rig. They don't increase your power above what your radio is rated, but they make your voice sound louder and generally carry further. Power mikes increase your modulation somewhat.

Fig. 2-4 Midland "Mic-ro-tune" remote channel selection (Courtesy Midland Int'l)

Mike Gain. This increases the strength of your modulation. Ask somebody for a radio check to tell you at what point your signal starts to distort or break up as you are increasing the volume. That will let you know where the best place is to run that thing.

P.A. The PA switch allows you to turn your CB into a public address system. There is a jack in the back where you can plug in a cord that runs to a loudspeaker. You can even put that loudspeaker under the bonnet or hood of your mobile if you want.

LED TX Lights. These small colored lights are used to indicate the proper functioning of the transmitter section on your CB.

Antenna Warning Light. If your antenna stops functioning properly, this light will come on when you transmit, to let you know that there's something wrong with the antenna.

Transmit Attenuator or High/Low Power. When switched on, this limits your transmit power to a fraction of what you would normally use. This is a popular feature on hand-held units that run off of battery power.

Making Something Out of the Advertising

Now suppose you are interested in getting a CB radio but don't know much about them. You could be strolling through the neighborhood shopping center and be surprised by a big display of CB radios. You try to stretch your imagination and comprehend all the advertising boasting of the quality of their inner workings, but it leaves you at a loss. Well, don't let that bog you down. Here are some common features you may run into:

Dual Conversion IF. A little fancier receive circuit that gives some added clarity of reception over a single conversion.

Filters. Ceramic, crystal lattice and mechanical; these are different ways of filtering your receiver in order to prevent bleeding over of a conversation on channels next to the one that you are using.

Automatic modulation compresser circuit (and limiter). This gizmo maintains a high level of modulation over a wide range of voice loudness. It also prevents over-modulation. A requirement on all new radios.

Type Accepted. Only radios marked *FCC Type Accepted* are legal to use in the United States. Definitely a consideration when buying one.

Type Approved. Only radios marked *Type Approved* by the Home Office are legal to use within the UK. This is indicated by an authorized stamp that is engraved onto the face of the radio.

Specifications. These are usually talked about with a lot of fancy figures thrown in that add to the confusion. When buying a new rig, you should try to get the best ratings you can.

Fig. 2-5 Realistic TRC-474 mobile CB radio (Courtesy Radio Shack Div. of Tandy)

US Type Accepted and *UK Type Approved* rigs should have ample selectivity for most applications and have equally good sensitivity. Selectivity is the receiver's ability to differentiate between an adjacent channel signal and the desired one, so folks aren't bleeding over on your channel. Adjacent Channel Rejection also has to do with this. Sensitivity is the measurement of how well your radio can hear. Good sensitivity can really make a difference for a base station and give you a longer range of reception. For mobile stations it is less critical since the ignition and static noise of the vehicle will sometimes drown out the weak stations that would have been picked up by a sensitive radio.

Here's a typical set of specs for a good quality rig and what they mean. **Once again, keep in mind that American CB radios will not have the FM functions, and British type-approved CB rigs will not offer the AM/SSB functions.**

THUNDERBOLT 3000
SPECIFICATIONS

Sensitivity - 0.5uV for 10 dB S + N/N; Selectivity - 6 kHz at −6dB; Adjacent Channel Rejection - 50 dB at ± 10 kHz; Squelch Sensitivity - .2 uV; Audio Power Output - 2 watts at 10% THD; FM Deviation - ±2.5 kHz; RF Power Output - 4 watts; AM Modulation - 90%; Spurious Output - −50 dB max.

AM Sensitivity (North America) - 0.5 uV for 10 dB S + N/N
Sensitivity gives you an idea how good it is pulling in a weak signal. The sensitivity, "uV" means microvolts—the lower the number, the better. The conditions are indicated by "dB S + N/N". It's the "signal plus noise-to-noise ratio." The larger the number of dBs, the better.

FM Sensitivity (Europe) - 0.3 uV for 20 dB noise quieting
A specification for European CB rigs, the FM sensitivity rating tells you the amount of signal at the antenna input necessary to be 20 dB stronger than the received noise level. This is the minimum signal that would fully quiet the background noise and make for a readable copy. Again the sensitivity is measured in microvolts and the lower the number here, the better.

Selectivity - 6 kHz at −6 dB
These two are related and they have to do with how clear your channel is going to sound if someone is using the channel next to yours. A lower figure here is better. They're usually between 5 and 6.

Adjacent Channel Rejection - 50 dB at ±10 kHz
Some manufacturers don't give selectivity the way it is here. They use the term Selectivity instead of Adjacent Channel Selection. A larger figure here is better, like 75 dB.

Frequency Tolerance - ±.003%
This gives an indication of how much the radio can drift off the channel, under normal operating conditions. On FM it is important to be as close as possible to the channel frequency for best operation. The lower this percentage, the better the stability of the radio will be.

Image Rejection - 60 dBs
Unwanted signals from above and below the CB band can penetrate into a receiver's IF section, interfering with what you can hear on the channel. The larger this figure, the more interference-free the radio's receiver will be from unwanted image frequencies. Dual conversion radios have much better image rejection than single conversion units.

Squelch Sensitivity - .2 uV
This is the minimum received signal at the antenna terminals that can trip the squelch control. This figure is slightly lower than the sensitivity ratings of the receiver. The lower this figure, the better.

Audio Power Output - 2 watts at 10% THD
The CB has a little amplifier just like a stereo and this is how much power it has to drive the speaker. The more watts, the louder that it can sound at full volume; 2 or 3 watts is plenty. This is the CB standard for clean sound. THD means Total Harmonic Distortion.

FM Deviation (Europe) - ±2.5 kHz
Another specification which applies to European CB rigs, the FM deviation indicates the amount of frequency shift above and below the channel frequency that is generated by FM modulation. 2.5 kHz deviation is a British Home Office standard.

RF Power Output - 4 watts RF power is the US and UK maximum.
The basic power of your transmitter. RF power output is how much radio frequency energy power actually comes out the coax connector of the radio when transmitting. The more the better.

AM Modulation - 90% typical
This is how much of the available talk power that North American CB transmitters actually use. While 100% is ideal, they can't cut it that close on an assembly line.

Spurious Output - −50 dB max.
This is the kind of garble that makes a mess on other channels, TV as well as CB. It's usually not mentioned. The larger the better.

Power Requirements - If you are getting a radio for your car, get one with a 12-14 volt DC rating. For a base station you can get a radio that runs off 120 (North America) or 240 (Europe) volts AC. Some companies make radios with dual power supplies for both mobile and base station operation. Positive or Negative ground (earth to British breakers) means it can be hooked up easily to either a positive or a negative ground vehicle.

Warranty

Every new radio should come with a warranty. The warranty guarantees the radio to be free from defects in materials and workmanship for a certain period of time, usually from three months to a year. There is a warranty registration card that you need to fill out and send back to the manufacturer within the first few days in order to register your radio. Also included is information on how to return the unit for repair under the warranty. In many instances, this involves returning it to the equipment dealer that sold you the unit. Make sure that you understand how this works. Don't forget to mail your card in!

Mobile or Base???

You can use a mobile radio as a base station by using a 12-volt DC converter that plugs into the wall. A mobile rig with a power converter will work just about as well as a more expensive base station radio would.

Now that you got past all that, you will want to try some of those fancy beauties on for size. Ask your dealer if you can try one. Grab that old microphone and ask some local CBer how you're getting out.

Buying a Used Rig

There are many used radios available, either through flea markets or classified ads in the newspapers. Many of these older CBs are of fine quality, but just don't have the compactness and extras that some of the new ones do. That's all right. Here is a way to get a good rig for a good price. You should see if it operates on transmit and receive. Make sure that the rig has the channels that you want. You may encounter 23-channel rigs left over from the days before the FCC legalized 40 channels for CB use in the U.S. Some of the walkie-talkies and really old rigs have plug-in crystals that are hard to find and you have to send away for them. So make sure you are getting the channels you want, or the crystals for the rig are easily available. Be aware that only radios marked *FCC Type Accepted* are legal for use in the US. Rigs manufactured before November 1978 may not have been type accepted.

Unless you are an antique dealer, stay away from the ancient tube-type mobile rigs. Transistors are best for mobile operations because 12 volt DC battery power is conveniently available. Long ago, transistors replaced tubes in mobiles not only because of their power efficiency but also because transistors exhibit more rugged performance in the face of vibrations and the bump and grind mobile traveling gives than tube radios would. However, a tube radio can still make a good base station. In fact, some of the more classic high-performance CB base stations like the *Browning Golden Eagles* are tube rigs. They run off of AC house current and can take certain kinds of electrical punishment (such as a high SWR or a direct antenna short) that would leave a transistor radio French-fried.

Some older tube base stations feature tunable receiving which lets you pull in different CB channels like you would tune in the stations on a short-wave radio. Some tube rigs may not have 100% modulation or full legal power and may need some pepping up or a power mike. You can have it tuned up by a qualified radio technician.

So how 'boutcha, Stump Jumper, you still on the channel?

Aye-4, I got my ears on. I just managed to make it through these pages, Mercy sakes!

Roger D. You getting familiar with that there hunk of junk?

10-4 on that. I've just been modulating on my buddy's rig here, and I think I'll go out and get myself one of these here squawk boxes.

Okay, guy. We'll catch you later. Ya got the Moonshiner, and we're out of here.

Chapter Three

Mobiles

CB has gotten as big as it has because of its great possibilities for communications while you're rolling down the road. It's great for talking back to your Home 20 and finding out how it's going back there, as well as getting connected with the flow of things out on the superslab. Since a lot of folks are going to want to start out with a rig in their four wheeler, we'll get right into how to install one in your car and mount a good antenna on it, too.

Installing Your CB

There are several good things to remember when you are going to put a new rig in your mobile. The first thing that comes to mind is where to mount it. This often depends on the driver's preference. There are some practical things, though, to keep in mind. You'll want it to be within easy reach and clearly visible when you're driving: you don't want to end up in the ditch because you had to dive for a mike to answer some local breaker. It should be out of the way of the gear shift or emergency brake. Make sure the mike cord and other wires won't get tangled up in the steering wheel or the accelerator and brake pedals, and that it is in a place where it won't get kicked or sat on. Also, heat can damage a rig, so don't mount it right under your car heater. It usually turns out that the rig is mounted somewhere under the dash close to the driver, or occasionally suspended from the roof near the driver.

Once you have figured out where you'd like to mount it, drill the holes for the mount, being careful not to hit anything behind the dashboard, and screw that bracket up there and bolt the CB onto it. Now is a good time to figure out how this rig is going to get its electricity. Most radios have two wires coming out of the back for the DC power: the red one and a black one. Usually, the red is positive (+) and black is negative (−). Most radios with two wires like this can be used for either positive or negative *ground (earth* to you British or Irish breakers) vehicles. (Check the instructions accompanying your radio to be sure.)

It's important to check to see whether your vehicle is positive or negative ground. Just lift up the hood and check to see which battery terminal is attached to the frame of the vehicle. Most cars are negative ground (the frame being ground) but **make sure first!!** Hooking your CB up the wrong way can damage it and set the ole set a smokin'.

Negative Ground Installations

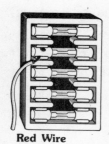

Red Wire

Fig. 3-1 Fuse box

Get some insulated wire like the kind sold at automobile parts stores for automotive wiring systems. Run it directly from the positive lead of the CB to the positive terminal of the car battery. Add an in-line fuse holder to this wire close to the battery to protect your car's electrical system. Make sure you tape all connections with good quality electrical tape. The negative wire can be bolted to the metal body of the car somewhere, because the negative terminal of the battery is also fastened to the metal. This ground connection will supply the negative connection to your radio.

The other way to do it is to tap into the car fuse panel (see picture). This makes it so you only have to run a wire from the fuse panel to the positive wire of the radio, a shorter distance than all the way to the battery.

It's a good idea to have a separate fuse for your CB. Most CBs come with a fuse in their supply lead. Never use anything bigger than a 3-amp fuse for a transistorized radio. Don't ever try to bypass your radio's fuse. Having a fuse can possibly save you some future repair bills by offering added protection. Don't transmit with your rig without an antenna made especially for CB connected to it. No other antenna will do; not the AM radio one; no, not your TV antenna either. Nope, only the real thing.

Positive Ground Installations

Some big trucks and semis are positive ground vehicles. Positive installations require another method of hooking up your radio. If you haven't got a rig yet, definitely check and see whether your vehicle is positive or negative ground. If it is positive ground, get a rig that can operate either way and it will save you a lot of trouble. Check the owners manual to determine if your radio can be operated in either a positive or negative ground vehicle.

Most radios have two small wires, one red and one black. In this case, just hook the red wire to some bolt or screw on the body of the vehicle. Hook the black wire through an in-line fuse holder to the negative terminal of the battery, or to a hot terminal in the fuse box.

Some radios just have one small wire coming out of the back. This is the hot lead. It is usually positive. This type of radio can only be used in a negative ground vehicle, because the case of the radio provides the negative ground connection. Some radios have a switch or can be rewired inside for positive ground operation. Read the instructions for this kind of radio carefully. Always make sure to use the proper fuse if you have to experiment.

If you have a vehicle with only 6 volts DC, there are 6 to 12 volt converters that you can buy in order to feed your rig the right menu.

Anti-theft Installations

Mobile CB radios just happen to be small, light, expensive and easy to rip off. Here are some suggestions which may help prevent this from happening to you. You don't want to lose your rig, for sure.

Your CB can be installed in such a way that you can easily remove it from under the dash and lock it in the trunk or take it into the house. One way to do this is to use a slide mount. This is the kind of mount that allows you to slide your rig in and out easily.

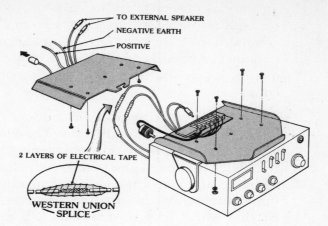

Fig. 3-2 Slide mount connections

TO EXTERNAL SPEAKER
NEGATIVE EARTH
POSITIVE

2 LAYERS OF ELECTRICAL TAPE

WESTERN UNION SPLICE

One section of the slide mount is attached to the mounting bracket of your radio, and the wires from the radio attach to a set of contacts on the slide mount. The other section is mounted in the vehicle and its contacts are wired into the vehicle's power and sometimes into the antenna. The two sections slide together and make contact. If you use one with the antenna connections on it, beware of the cheaper models that do not make good enough connection, resulting in high SWR which can lead to a radio burnout.

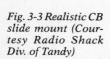

Fig. 3-3 Realistic CB slide mount (Courtesy Radio Shack Div. of Tandy)

If you prefer to keep your radio in your mobile, you can get a locking mount that makes it so you need a key to take the rig off the mount. There are also easy-to-install car burglar alarm systems available at electronics stores. Some burglar alarm systems honk your horn or ring an alarm inside your car when the door or hood is opened, or if your radio is taken from its mount. When you leave it in your mobile be sure to lock the doors.

There are several disguised CB antennas that are made to look like regular car radio antennas. These can be quite handy in preventing radio thieves from knowing what you have in your vehicle. Some have a junction box which allows you to plug your CB radio and your car's long and medium wave radio into the same antenna. Within the junction box, there are some tuned circuits which help to match the CB to the antenna. Usually these circuits are adjusted after installations, with the aid of a SWR meter. The trouble with this accessory is that you end up losing some of your power right there in the junction box. Also, if these circuits aren't just right, you won't get out well at all, and could even damage your rig.

There are kinds of disguised antennas that use no matcher and are not to be connected to your car radio. They perform much better because the antenna is pretuned at the factory for CB frequencies. All of your transmitter power goes directly to the antenna without going through any junction box or splitter. And best of all, they look just like the standard car antenna which they replace. In order to get your car radio back to receiving your favorite DJs, you can get an AM/FM antenna that adheres to the glass of your back window.

IT'S TEN O:CLOCK...
DO YOU KNOW WHERE
YOUR RIG IS?

Mobile Antennas

Fig. 3-4 (Right) Midland luggage rack, "rubber duckie" and mirror-mount cophased twin antennas (Courtesy Midland Int'l)

Fig. 3-5 (Below) Mobile CB antennas

The heart of CB communications is mobile-to-mobile and mobile-to-base operations. The antenna that you have on your mobile definitely helps to determine just how far you will get out. One thing to keep in mind is that all antennas designed to operate on 27 MHz will work equally well on AM or SSB—the North American CB standards, or FM—the European CB standard. (Antennas for the new British & Irish FM frequencies, however, will need to be a tad shorter in physical length than their American equivalents.)

There are many different kinds of mounts and places you can put your antenna. You could stick that ear just about any place on your mobile, but some places have advantages over others.

The metal body of your vehicle is actually a part of your antenna. The location of the antenna in relation to the car body will affect the radiation pattern of your signal, which will be the strongest across the longest portion of the vehicle.

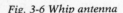

Fig. 3-6 Whip antenna

Whips

By far the best physical length for a 27 MHz CB antenna which would still be practical for mobile use would be 2.5 meters (100″) long. Although we've seen these big twigs on the tops of some vehicles, they tend to mix it with the tree limbs and garage roofs, etc. So 2.5 meter whips are usually mounted on the back bumpers. A 2.5 meter whip is equal to a quarter wavelength for 27 MHz. This whip, when mounted on the back bumper, uses the car body as part of the antenna and works best in the direction towards the front of the car. As a general rule concerning mobile antennas, the longer the better. And the higher on the vehicle you mount one, the better it will get out.

CBers who live outside of North America should keep in mind that some countries restrict the overall length of CB antennas. In Great Britain, for example, the Home Office has set a limit on the length of all 27 MHz antennas to 1.5 meters (59″) or less. So this is the longest you can legally use in the UK—for base as well as mobile antennas! This short length makes the 1.5 meter whip a less efficient antenna when compared to the longer ones in use in other parts of the world.

Loading Coils

A loading coil is a coil of wire imbedded in a plastic cylinder. For shortened antennas, (any antenna less than 2.5 meters in length), the loading coil makes up the difference for the missing length. In the case of a 1.5 meter whip, the loading coil electrically replaces one meter of the total ¼ wavelength of 2.5 meters. The loading coil is connected to the hot center conductor of the coax, and the steel whip or stinger is sticking out of the coil.

For those cases where a 2.5 meter whip is not practical, a shorter whip antenna should be used. These short whips come in many varieties, but they can be divided into 3 main groups: base loaded steel whips, center or top-loaded steel whips, and wire-wound fiberglass whips.

Base-Loaded Steel Whips

Fig. 3-7 (Above) Loading coil

Fig. 3-8 (Right) Base-loaded steel whip

Base-loaded steel whips are generally very durable and inconspicuous. While they do not get out as well as a big twig or a top-loaded antenna would, they do quite well for talking local, and have been used by CBers around the world for years. When mounting a base-loaded antenna, keep in mind that the base coil radiates much of your signal, so it should be placed in a position clear of surrounding metal surfaces. The roof, hood or trunk lip, or fender are the most common mounting points.

Center or Top-Loaded Steel Whips

Fig. 3-9 Center loaded steel whip

The center- or top-loaded whip is the next best thing to a full sized twig. They come in many shapes, styles, and colors. The loaded coil in the center or near the top of the antenna is more electrically efficient than base loading for getting that signal in the air. Stainless steel is the best for long term durability. Some top-loaded whips have an aluminum shaft that can be prone to bending. An impact spring at the bottom might be a good idea if your particular installation is likely to encounter low tree branches, etc. Then your antenna's survival might depend on it!

Most loaded whips have a top section or stinger that can be adjusted in length for tuning the antenna.

Fiberglass Whips

The wire-wound fiberglass whip has become very popular in recent years. It comes in many lengths and colors. The most popular is the 1.2-meter (4-foot) whip. As a general rule, the longer the whip is, the better it will get out, whether or not it is called a ¼-, ⅝-, ¾- or full-wave mobile antenna. A full-length ¼-wave fiberglass whip is 2.5 meters (100″) long. A base spring is recommended when using some fiberglass antennas. Fiberglass whips generally come tuned up from the factory and need little or no adjustment in their length. These antennas have a wire imbedded in the fiberglass that actually does the radiating of your CB signal.

This wire is sometimes wound spirally up the fiberglass rod, forming a continuous loading coil. Of all the short antennas available, this one gets out the best. Some of the helically-wound fiberglass whips look very much like conventional AM car antennas, and are also very popular.

Fig. 3-10 Fiberglass whip

Twin Antennas

Twins are very popular on semis, RVs and other vehicles where it is not possible to mount a single antenna on the roof. Two identical antennas are used with a special set of coaxial cables called a co-phase harness. This is nothing more than two equal lengths of coax, both hooked to the same connector.

The two antennas combine together to provide a directional signal. If the antennas are at least 2.5 meters (100″) apart, such as on two mirrors of a big semi, they will get out best forwards and backwards. If they are less then 2.5 meters apart, they will get out sideways, something you wouldn't want when you're driving down the superslab. Remember that whenever you use twin antennas you end up sacrificing some directions in favor of others. It's not wise to use gutter mount twins on a car because you get out sideways. You would be better off using a base loaded antenna on the roof or trunk of your car, or just a single gutter mount.

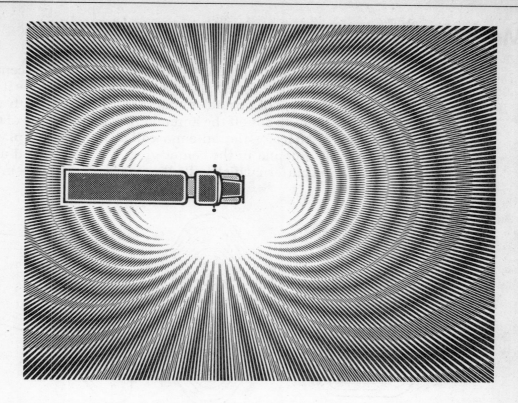

Fig. 3-11 Trucker's twins radiation pattern

Mobile Antennas for UHF CB Operation

In the United Kingdom, the government has established a second CB service using UHF frequencies. On 934 MHz, the antenna's length is much shorter, usually less then 0.25 meters long. The antenna must be mounted on the top of the vehicle, clear from any obstructions (i.e. luggage racks, car aerials, etc.), for good results. Due to more exacting technical aspects, we recommend that the installation and maintenance of 934 MHz stations be left to experienced radio technicians.

Mounts

The best place to put a single antenna is smack dab in the center of the roof. This is the highest place you can put it. This gets it up and out of the way of obstacles that could interfere with the radio waves coming out off the antenna. The metal frame of the car is used as part of the antenna called the ground plane. Mounting the antenna in the center gives a balanced and uniform radiation pattern which will allow you to get out well in all directions.

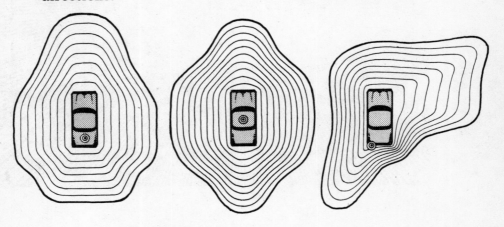

Fig. 3-12 Antenna radiation patterns

A mount is a device that hooks your antenna onto your vehicle. Mounts are usually made of metal and have a plastic part which electrically insulates the whip from the metal. There are many kinds of mounts, almost as many as there are antennas. The most popular ones are the boot or truck lip mount and the rain gutter clip mount. The rain gutter mount is good for getting your antenna up high where it can get out. The trunk lip mount can also be used for mounting to the hood.

An important thing to remember with any mount is that it must have a good electrical connection between the mount and the car body. Some mounts have an adjustable set screw which is tightened until the pointed end of the screw pokes through the body paint, electrically bonding the mount to the vehicle. Some other mounts require boring a hole through the body of your vehicle. Now don't cringe, for heaven's sake. It isn't that bad. This is the strongest method of mounting a mobile aerial.

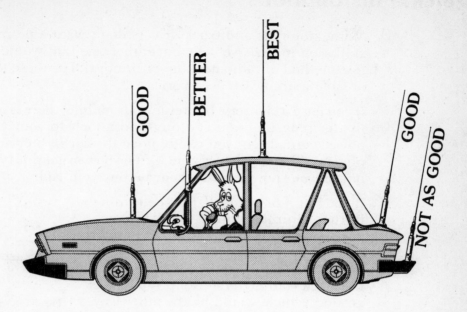

Fig. 3-13 Antenna locations

The mirror/luggage rack mount is a good mount to use if one fits your vehicle. Bumper mounts are useful for putting longer twigs on coupes or small cars.

The center conductor of the coax connects to the whip either directly, or through a loading coil. Neither the whip nor the center conductor should touch other metal. If you think that the whip might touch the metal body when your vehicle is in motion, you can insulate the section of the whip with some electrical tape or plastic tubing. Avoid installations where the antenna whip is up next to the vehicle's body for over a ½ meter (1.5 feet) of the whip's total length. This type of installation will often produce a high SWR which cannot be tuned out and will result in inferior performance.

By all means, follow directions enclosed with the mount you use. Most problems can be avoided by just reading the instructions. Special attention should be paid when drilling holes to make sure that the exact size drill bit is used.

Quickie Installations

Many motorists and truck drivers don't want a permanent installation in their vehicle, but rather one that would permit a fast method of radio hook-up or removal. For these folks there are a few simple CB accessories.

If you have a cigarette lighter in your mobile, there is a cigarette lighter plug that you can buy, and attach to your CB's radio power cord. Then, you can remove the car lighter and simply plug into the vehicle's system. Often you can get this type of plug put on your power cord when you buy your radio.

If you put it on yourself, first determine if the vehicles you'll be using are positive or negative ground. In a negative ground vehicle, the red power lead would attach to the tip of the plug, and the black lead to the side clip. A positive ground vehicle would be the other way around.

Fig. 3-14 Cigarette lighter plug

The best way to attach the wires to the plug is by soldering them on. If you don't know how to solder, there is a section later in the book that can help you out. When you are done, make sure that the red and black leads from the power cord remain insulated from each other, back where they enter the cigarette lighter plug. If you plan on switching from one vehicle to another with this set-up, make sure that they all have the same ground, or damage to the radio may result.

Quickie Mounts

There are magnetic mount antennas that magnetically hold the antenna down onto any steel roof. They are great for the instant installation; you just run the coax through the window or in through the trunk or boot. A magnetic mount will withstand winds up to 172 kilometers (120 miles) per hour and will work either on the roof or trunk. Magnet mounts don't get out as well as some other kinds of antennas that are electrically connected to the chassis. But for someone on the move, they could be just the thing.

Do not cut the coax short on a magnet mount or bunch the coax up into a bundle, because the antenna will not get out nearly as well. On a magnet mount, the coax itself is part of the antenna. Also, be careful not to use a magnet mount near a luggage rack or other metal obstructions as it makes it harder to tune up. Some semi tractor bodies are made of aluminum, which makes it impossible to use a magnetic mount on the cab.

Emergency Mobile Installations

Many CB manufacturers now provide a complete emergency CB kit that can be stowed away conveniently in the trunk or under the driver's seat. Contained within a plastic carrying case is a tiny CB antenna with a magnetic base, a 40-channel CB radio and a radio power cord equipped with a cigarette lighter plug. In the event of a road mishap, the installation of one of these units is quickly accomplished by plugging the power cord into the cigarette lighter opening and screwing the antenna's coaxial connector to the antenna plug on the back of the CB radio.

Fig. 3-15 Realistic magnet mount antenna (Courtesy Radio Shack Div. of Tandy)

Fig. 3-16 Midland Emergency Rescue Kit (Courtesy Midland Int'l)

Fig. 3-17 Uniden Pro 310E CB Emergency Kit (Courtesy Uniden)

This type of emergency unit has proven to be very popular among individuals who otherwise might have had no interest in CB radio. In the event of an emergency, the unit can provide a way to obtain assistance from nearby motorists, police or local garage services that monitor channel 19. The main limitation of these emergency mobile installations is that they usually come with fairly short antennas which limit their effective range to just a few miles. Although they require permanent installation, full-sized regular CB mobile antennas usually can triple the range of communications over the reach of emergency units—an important benefit for those that frequently travel through sparsely-populated rural areas.

Hooking Up The Coax

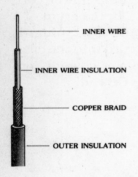

INNER WIRE

INNER WIRE INSULATION

COPPER BRAID

OUTER INSULATION

Fig. 3-18 Coax elements

O.K. We have gotten the radio wired up. Now we have to hook up that radio to an ear. In order for the radio signal to get from the CB to the antenna, you need some kind of wire to connect them together. Usually, a special kind of two-conductor shielded wire is used, called coax (Koh-axe, from coaxial). This special wire is made up of an inner wire covered with a plastic sheath, and outer wire mesh that in turn is covered by a black outer covering. Now there are several types of coax, but only two kinds are much good for CB—RG-58/U and RG-8/U coax. Unless you're running 1000 watts in your mobile, RG-58/U will work fine.

RG-59/U is sometimes used for twin CB antenna phasing harnesses. It should never be used for single antenna CB installations.

It's good when installing a CB to get the coax up and out of the way, not only for looks, but also to keep it from getting stepped on or tripped over. Avoid flattening or crimping or wearing the insulation off.

The coax will need to be connected to the back of the radio and to the antenna. This is done with a connector (such as a PL 259) that attaches to the coax.

The coax and connector are often supplied when you buy an antenna. Sometimes, though, you may need to attach your own connector, especially if you make your own antenna. We talk about attaching connectors to coax later in the book.

Connecting the Coax to the Antenna

Some antennas have the coax already attached. Other antennas either have a connector that plugs into the base of the antenna or the two terminals which attach to the antenna mount. There are a few other ways to do this, so check the instructions that came with your antenna.

It is important that the shield of the coax be securely connected to the body of your vehicle. The shield is the larger outside braided wire on the coaxial cable. Usually, the mount of the antenna provides this connection. If you are using a mirror mount type, make sure that your mirror braces are making good connections with the body of the truck.

Sometimes if the connection is not made properly, the antenna will not work right. Although you may be able to receive somewhat, you may not get out very well. Sometimes scraping down to bare metal is necessary in order to make a good connection.

SWR—Is your Antenna Working Right?

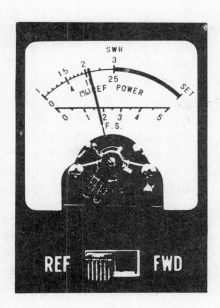

Fig. 3-19 SWR meter

The length of your antenna makes a difference. Even though we can't see them, the radio waves have an actual physical length. You must match your antenna's length to that of the CB radio wave. When your antenna is the wrong length, some of the power does not radiate, but is bounced back into the coax, and into the radio itself. If this reflected power is too high, it can cause your CB's power transistors to overheat and even burn up! Besides, it's a waste of energy that could get out there and do its thing for you. So you want the least amount of reflected power and the most amount of forward power you can get.

SWR means Standing Wave Ratio. Sounds rather high falootin', don't it? Well don't let it scare you off. It's simple. You can find if your antenna is the right length by using an SWR meter. An SWR meter can be purchased at most radio stores or borrowed from another CBer.

Checking SWR

First of all, you'll need a short coaxial cable with a connector on each end. Plug in one connector into your rig and the other into the socket on the meter labeled TXMTR or TX. Plug the coax that goes to your antenna into the socket on your meter labeled ANT.

Turn the knob on the meter all the way down (counterclockwise). Put the switch in the forward or calibrate position. Turn on your radio and listen for other stations. It should be working normally. Tune your channel selector to some unused channel where you won't bother anyone.

Press your mike button and, without saying anything into the mike, adjust the knob on the SWR meter until the meter reads set, or full scale. Then flip the switch to Reflected or SWR and read the SWR scale of your meter.

After noting what the SWR is, stop transmitting. If the meter reads less than 1.5, your antenna is working properly. If it reads more than 2, your antenna probably needs some adjustment. If it reads more than 3 or in the red, check all connections at the antenna for possible bad connections; the antenna or the center wire of the coax might be touching the body of the vehicle. Coiling your excess coax into a small bundle can cause a high standing wave. If this happens, the coax can be coiled into longer loops to avoid causing a high SWR.

When installing a truck lip antenna, make sure you scrape the paint away on the underside of the trunk or hood lid where the little set screws make contact. A poor ground connection here is a major cause of high SWR. If you obtain a high SWR when installing mirror mounts or luggage-rack mount antennas, check and make sure that the mirrors or luggage rack is grounded to the body of the vehicle. A poor ground here will also give you SWR problems. Antennas shorter than about .5 meters (1.5 feet) long will probably have a high SWR or not work quite as well on some channels than others. A short antenna will not tune a broad enough range of frequencies to include all forty channels.

Adjusting Your Antenna

So let's say that your SWR turns out to be 2:1, and you want to bring it down. There are two ways to change an antenna's SWR: one is to lengthen it, and the other is to shorten it. You can figure out which way to go in the following manner: Take an SWR reading on channel 1, then take one on channel 40. Which channel had the higher SWR? If the SWR is higher on channel 40, you need to shorten the tip. If the SWR was higher on channel 1, you need to lengthen the tip. Move it about ¼" at a time. Check the SWR on some of the middle channels and try to set the antenna so that it has the lowest SWR on the middle channels.

Most antennas have a set screw you can loosen so that the tip can slide up and down. If this does not give enough adjustment, you can clip or file ¼" at a time off the bottom of the tip and reinsert it in the coil. Make sure to reset the SWR meter every time you take a reading.

One good rule to remember when adjusting the antenna's length is, if you bring your hand near the loading coil or the top of the antenna and the SWR goes down, the tip of the antenna needs to be lengthened; if the SWR goes up, the tip needs to be shortened. If you're using twins, make equal adjustments to each side at the same time.

Don't cut too much off, now!

If the SWR is high, do not hold the mike button in for more than 10 seconds at a time. This will protect the power transistors from possible burn-out.

Fig. 3-20 Setting antenna length

Chapter Four

Base Stations

Break Lancelot! Rapunzel's calling. Did you stop at the bakery for me yet? C'mon.

Base stations are extremely popular because they provide breakers with free communications to other bases and mobile stations as well. Whether you are into base operating for the late night ratchet, emergency monitoring, or for contacts from your mobile to the home twenty, a CB set-up can be a great thing to have. Within just about every good sized community there are base operators on the air giving directions and local information, as well as keeping the community informed of who's where and what's happening.

How about it, Test Pilot? Did you copy Blue Dog on his way to Mule Town, C'mon?

Negatory. I don't believe he's been by this twenty yet. I've been copying the mail all morning, trying out a new base station, c'mon.

Roger Dee. Well, if you hear him on the channel, tell him that Screamin' Demon was looking for an eyeball, and we'll try him next time through, c'mon!

That's a four. We'll give you the golden numbers then. Have a safe one. This is the old Test Pilot Base going down and gone.

Installing a Base Station

A base station unit is a little different from a mobile rig. It's usually bigger, and it runs on 120 volts AC (240 volts AC in Europe and other locations outside North America), so you can plug in right off the main power. You can set it up on a desk or bookshelf, somewhere you find easily accessible and easy to

Fig. 4-1 Realistic Navaho CB base station (Courtesy Radio Shack Div. of Tandy)

monitor. Installing it is no problem: hook up an antenna and coax, and you're in business. It is important, however, to connect your base station to a good solid antenna that will maximize your signal output.

Fig. 4-2 Uniden Pro 710E CB base station (Courtesy Uniden)

Using a Mobile Rig as a Base

If you plan on using a mobile rig for a base station, you will need to hook up an AC to DC power supply or a 12-volt DC auto or motorcycle battery and charger. Since mobile rigs are rather small and lightweight, we suggest that you mount the rig on a table, desk, shelf or a block of wood, to hold it down. If you plan to use a DC converter, make sure you get one with at least a 3 amp. capacity at 12 to 14 volts DC. Also, make sure that the supply is regulated.

The DC power supply is usually a small box that plugs into an AC outlet and has two terminals where you can attach the radio's power leads. To hook up your radio, connect the red lead from the transceiver to the positive (+) terminal and the black to the negative (−) terminal. If your radio has no black lead, use a piece of insulated automotive-type wire to connect a screw on

Fig. 4-3 CB mobile-as-base wiring diagram

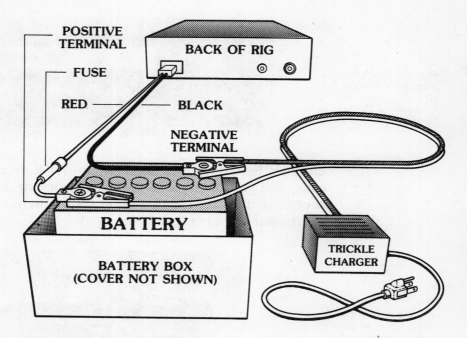

the radio's case to the negative terminal of the DC power converter. Make sure there is a 2- or 3-amp fuse inserted between the power converter and the radio.

Since a CB radio can serve as a valuable communications tool if your AC power fails, some CBers may be interested in using a battery pack as a power source instead on an AC-to-DC power converter. Additionally, some AC-operated CB base stations come with the option of operating off of 12 volts DC as well. Then if you should have an AC power failure, your base will continue to operate on battery power automatically. A transistorized CB transceiver will run about a week or two under normal use on a fully charged car battery.

If you plan to use an automobile or motorcycle battery instead of a DC converter you should get something to keep it in. Battery acid can and will eat your clothes and lots of other things, including your rug. There are plastic cases sold for use with electric boat motors that are available at hardware stores. Whatever you put the battery in, make sure that you have adequate ventilation. Batteries let off hydrogen gas, which, if allowed to build up, can be ignited by a spark or flame, causing an explosion. Batteries should also be well out of the reach of small children, as the acid within them can cause burns and other injuries. If you are buying a new battery, try to get a sealed maintenance-free battery. This is the safest kind to use.

Hooking Up the Battery and Charger

The battery should be located within fifteen feet or so from the radio, so you don't lose too much juice running through long wires. You will need the following components in order to complete the installation:

- 12 volt car battery and case.
- 1 to 2 amp trickle charger (auto parts or department store).
- Two insulated wires of different colors, each long enough to reach from battery to the radio.
- Electrical tape.
- One positive battery clamp with wing nut.
- One negative battery clamp with wing nut.
- An in-line fuse holder with 3-amp fuse.

Make sure you get the right wires on the right battery posts.

Home Twenty Aerials

Getting yourself a good set of ears is one of the most important aspects of getting out. You can go and buy commercially-made antennas that will do a good job for you. Or you can construct and install your own. We have included some antenna projects later on in the book that can save you some money and serve as an entertaining way to learn more about the fascinating realm of radio communications.

Particular antenna designs are often identified by their *wave-length*. A wavelength is the length in space of one complete cycle of any radio wave. This length will differ depending on the frequency of the radio signal. One wavelength for 27 MHz CB frequencies would be about 11 meters (about 35 feet) long! That's why the CB band is often referred to as the 11-meter band. Most CB base station antennas are physically a multiple or submultiple of this length, because that is the right size package for catching this particular radio wave.

Driving around these days, you can notice all kinds, shapes, and sizes of base station antennas. The people that transmit through them talk about how well their aerials do, and you might wonder what kind of difference one could have over another as far as getting out goes. Obviously, you're bound to get out better the higher you go, so stick it on up there!

Another thing you hear people talk about is gain.

Gain

The simplest antenna, a regular ¼ wave vertical, has no gain. Manufacturers call this unity gain. Other antennas that we talk about are measured by determining how many times better than this they are. Let's say that you just bought a new antenna that has a gain of 3 dBs (dB stands for decibels, a mathematical term used when comparing two power levels). When you hook up your rig to this new antenna, you'll increase your effective power past what a ¼ wave vertical antenna could put out. A 3 dB gain represents a doubling of power. Here's a chart that has the gain all worked out for you.

dB Gain	Multipy Power by
0	1.0
1	1.2
2	1.6
3	2.0
4	2.5
5	3.0
6	4.0
7	5.0
8	6.3
9	8.0
10	10.0
11	12.6
12	15.
13	20.0
14	25.1
15	31.6
16	40.0
17	50.2
18	63.2
19	80.0
20	100.4

If you had a new antenna with a gain of 6 dB, and your radio was putting 4 watts into it, your new aerial would have generated a signal level that would be the equivalent of running 16 watts into a ¼ wave antenna.

One of the best twigs you can get for a base rig has a gain of 13 dB. If you put 4 watts of output power into that, you would send the equivalent of 80 watts of output power in the direction that the antenna is pointed. A change of one decibel in power is a just noticeable change in loudness. It takes about 6 dB of gain to move an S-meter one unit. In other words, if you are using a regular ¼ wave and then switch to a beam that has 6 dB of gain the signals that you transmit and receive will be stronger by one notch on your and the other station's S-meters.

The gain we're talking about actually has to come from somewhere. In an *omnidirectional* antenna (works well in all horizontal directions), gain comes from building the antenna in such a way that the RF energy is spread out closer and flatter to the ground. This puts more of your power into radio waves that travel along the earth's surface. It does this by taking power away from higher angles that otherwise would radiate part of the signal uselessly into space. Most local communications are done via the ground wave which is why some types of omnidirectional antennas are called *ground planes*.

The other kind of antenna that's directional is the beam which focuses the RF energy narrowly, by the use of several antenna elements. This gain is produced at the expense of RF energy that could have gone in other directions.

Effective Radiated Power

The amount of power legally allowed for CB transmissions actually varies from country to country. In the U.S., for example, CB stations are allowed to transmit a maximum of 4 watts of output power. In Britain, the Home Office has limited the *Effective Radiated Power*, or ERP of all 27 MHz FM stations to 2 watts. The ERP of any CB station is equal to the amount of power actually reaching the antenna multiplied by the amount of gain that the antenna has. This takes into account the amount of power lost in the coax between the radio and the antenna. The attenuation chart below outlines several ways that you can lose dBs between the radio and the coax.

Attenuation Chart

Losses in dB	Source	Losses in dB	Source
-½ dB	for every coax connector in the line	-2½ dB	for every 100 feet of RG-58 between the radio and the antenna
-1 dB	for every SWR meter, switch, or other add-on device in the line	-1 dB	for every 100 feet of RG-8 between the radio and the antenna

If you have an in-line SWR meter, you lose a −½ dB for each coax connector on either side of the meter, and −1 dB for the meter itself. Even a run of only 40 feet of RG-58 coax will lose you another 1 dB. With a set-up like this you would lose 3 dB, so only half of your original power would actually reach the antenna. Of course, if you used a high gain antenna, you could boost your signal level back up again. In the United Kingdom and elsewhere in Europe, however, CB antenna length has been limited by law to 1.5 meters or less. In fact the 1.5 meter CB antenna has an actual loss factor of around 3 dB. This makes it quite impossible for any base station to even put out 2 watts of ERP, even if the antenna was mounted right on top of the base station. Unfortunately, the 1.5 meter antenna will also be less sensitive on receive than any of the longer antennas would be.

In the United Kingdom, the government has also legalized a second CB service operating via UHF frequencies. On the 934 MHz FM Band, stations are allowed to run up to 25 watts ERP. Because of some of the limitations of UHF, the Home Office has allowed multi-element beam antennas to be used for the base station installations.

Ground, Space, and Sky Waves

On 27 MHz, there are three different paths by which CB radio waves can travel from one location to another. These paths are often referred to as the ground wave, the space wave and the sky wave.

The Ground Wave. CB radio signals are conducted by the ground along the surface of the earth. Ground-wave signals actually can bend around buildings and go over hills.

The Space Wave. When two stations are within line of sight of each other, they can communicate point to point via the space

Fig. 4-4 Ground/ space/sky waves

The Ground Wave

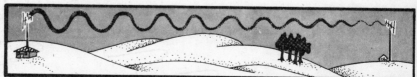

The Space Wave

The Sky Wave

wave. If you can remember that radio waves are similar to visible light, then it is clear that any locations you can see from your antenna's perch, you can also talk to. (British users of the 934 MHz CB band should keep in mind that since UHF frequencies are so short, 934 MHz CB radio waves can only travel via the space waves.)

The Sky Wave. This is the path by which long distance (DX) communications take place. All skip signals utilize that part of the radio signal which shoots upward at a sharp enough angle to permit the earth's ionosphere to reflect it back down to earth. By this path, radio waves can span great distances, from several hundred to several thousand miles. While ground and space wave signals travel equally well throughout the day or year, sky wave conduction of radio waves depends on whether the sun has charged the upper atmosphere sufficiently. That's why DX communications on CB frequencies can only take place at certain times. (On UHF the radio waves are so short that they never are reflected, but just pass on through into space.)

Polarization

Depending on the position of the antenna, radio waves travel with either vertical (elements straight up and down) or horizontal (lying flat) polarization. Vertically-polarized antennas get out via the ground wave much better than horizontal ones.

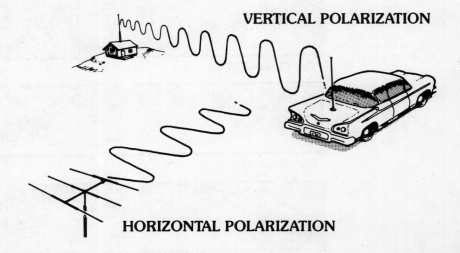

VERTICAL POLARIZATION

HORIZONTAL POLARIZATION

Fig. 4-5 Polarizations

That's why all CB mobiles are vertically polarized. Most base station ears are vertical or have both horizontal and vertical antennas.

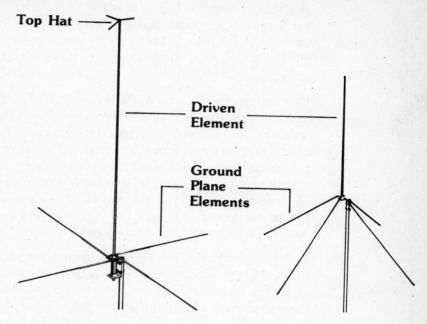

Top Hat

Driven Element

Ground Plane Elements

Fig. 4-6 Pictured on the left is a ⅝ Wavelength Vertical Antenna with a top hat. On right is a ¼ Wavelength Vertical Antenna.

A horizontally-polarized antenna will not pick up the signal generated by a vertically-polarized antenna nearly as well as a vertical aerial would. For communications between two base stations, however, it is sometimes useful to use horizontal polarization, because there will be less interference from other stations trying to use the same channel. In this case, both stations need to be using horizontally-polarized antennas. DX CB stations have found that the polarity of the antenna is not important; after reflection off the ionosphere, a radio wave can return to earth at any polarization. The results are unpredictable.

Whether you are buying an antenna or building one yourself, your first decision must be whether you want to put up a directional beam antenna or an omnidirectional vertical antenna. An omnidirectional antenna could give equal coverage for all directions locally, while a beam antenna would give you a longer range, but only in one direction at a time. Of course, you can always get a TV rotator to put on that beam antenna so you can point it in whatever direction you want. Or you might want both a beam and a vertical antenna for use at different times.

The ¼ Wave Vertical Ground Plane Antennas

The most basic CB antenna is the ¼ wavelength vertical antenna. A ¼ wave ground plane has a 1 dB gain above an isotropic source, which is an imaginary antenna used by radio engineers for electrical gain measurements. It gets out fairly well in all directions.

This antenna consists of a driven vertical element and three or four radials that act as the ground plane. The driven element receives the transmit energy from the rig, while the radials act as a counterbalancing ground. A ¼ wave vertical can be mounted very easily, and takes up very little room. It can be installed on a lightweight metal pole or pipe such as used for a TV antenna, or right on the roof or the side of a chimney. You can get an inexpensive "push-up" type pole, up to 50 feet tall, that a couple of breakers can put up easily.

There are other ¼ wavelength antennas that are not ground planes. They usually work about the same as a ground plane. In order for an omnidirectional antenna to have any gain, it must have a driven element longer than 6 meters (about 20 feet). Beware of ¼ wave ground planes advertising 5 dB gain!!

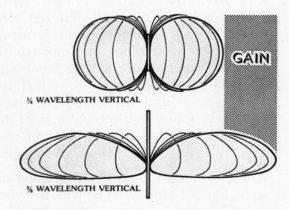

Fig. 4-7 Vertical gain

¼ WAVELENGTH VERTICAL

GAIN

⅝ WAVELENGTH VERTICAL

The ⅝ Wavelength Vertical Antenna

The ⅝ wavelength vertical is similar to the ¼ wavelength vertical antenna. It too has a radiating element and three or four radials. However, the ⅝ wavelength's driven element is much longer. This is because ⅝ of a wavelength is much longer than ¼ of a wavelength. This extra length has an effect on how the radio energy is focused. This is what gain is all about, effectively using all the energy that is there. The main thing about a ⅝ wavelength is that it focuses its power low to the ground. A ⅝ wavelength antenna will usually have a 3 to 4.5 dB gain over a ¼ wavelength antenna. This can increase your range as much as 10 kilometers (about 6 miles) or more, taking advantage of energy that otherwise would go up and be useless, both for local and long distance communications.

There are other omnidirectional antennas that will work similar to the ⅝ or ¼ wavelength antenna. The respective gain ratings of the various antennas provide one of the ways for you to compare different units.

Beams

Directional antennas, or beams, are made up of multiple elements. An element is a length of tubing or wire positioned in such a way as to make radio waves travel in a certain direction. Usually, the more elements an antenna has, the more gain it has, and the better it will cut out interference from unwanted directions.

There are three types of antenna elements. The *driven* element is hooked directly to your coaxial cable and is the one that directly radiates the power from your transmitter. The *reflector* element is usually slightly longer than the driven element and is positioned about 1.5 meters (approximately 5 feet) behind the driven element. It acts like a mirror behind the driven element to reflect waves in the direction that the antenna is pointing. On the other side of the driven element are one or more *directors*, which are usually slightly shorter than the driven element. It acts like a lens to intensify the energy in the direction the antenna is pointed. Additional director elements will also increase the gain of the antenna even further.

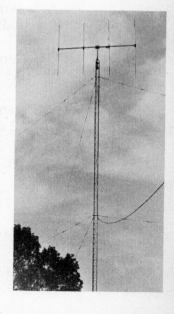

Fig. 4-8   4-element CB beam

Vertical Beams

This is the most common type of CB beam. Vertical beams work well for both local and longer distance communications. They are usually made of lightweight aluminum tubing and require the use of a motorized assembly in order to position the beam. Some of these beams are small enough to be turned by a TV rotator. Others, like the *Phased Vertical Array* are physically fixed in place yet change directions electronically with the flip of a switch.

When putting up a beam, try to keep it as far from other metal objects and antennas as possible. They could interfere with the beam's operation. Usually the vertical elements are about 5 meters (17 feet) long and are supported by a larger-diameter aluminum pipe called a boom. Generally speaking, the longer the boom, the higher the antenna gain.

Maximum
Gain:

3 element
8 dB

4 element
10.5 dB

5 element
12 dB

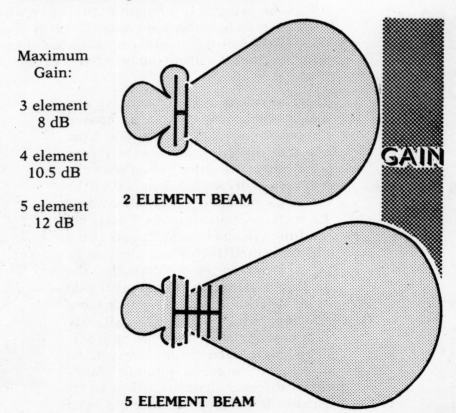

2 ELEMENT BEAM

GAIN

5 ELEMENT BEAM

Fig. 4-9 Beam gain

Stacked Beams

Stacking beams gives you more gain than just having one. Keep in mind that you will need a sturdy tower to hold one of these babies up, and a heavy-duty rotator to move it. The beams have to be at least 7 meters (17 feet) apart for maximum gain to be realized. This wide spacing actually increases the total *capture area* of the antenna. A special co-phase harness will need to be used that combines the inputs for both driven elements (one for each beam in the stack) together so that a single coaxial cable can be connected to the antenna connection of the base station transceiver.

Approximate gains of stacked beams:
    3 + 3 = 11.5 dB
    4 + 4 = 13.5 dB
    5 + 5 = 15 dB

Mercy sakes!

Fig. 4-10 Stacked beams

Switchable Horizontal/Vertical (Criss-Cross) Beams

These beams combine two identical antennas on the same boom, with one antenna having a horizontal orientation and the other a vertical one. Each beam will have its own coax. A coaxial switch is used to change from one to the other. Keep in mind that an 8-element criss-cross beam has only 4 active elements at a time.

Quads

Quad antennas use loop or square elements, usually made of wire and supported on an X-shaped frame. Usually, a quad has more gain per element than a regular rod-type aerial. Like regular beam antennas, the quad antennas are highly directional and will need some kind of rotator for changing their position. Like Criss-Cross beams, some quads have two driven elements so that switchable polarization can be achieved.

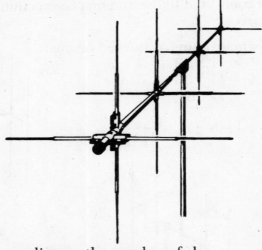
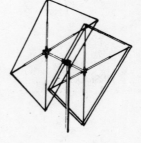

Fig. 4-11 Criss-cross and quad beams

Depending on the number of elements and the spacing, the following gains are possible:

2 elements: 8.5 dB;   4 elements: 13.5 dB;
3 elements: 11.5 dB;   5 elements: 15 dB.

Like their rod-type counterparts, quads also can be stacked for more gain. Because of their large capture area, they are one of the best beams around. However, this same area can also "capture" more wind, making it more susceptible to weather damage. If you decide to buy a quad antenna, be sure that it is manufactured out of rugged, high quality materials. Remember that a quad will also need a stout tower to provide sufficient support during all kinds of weather conditions.

Coax

When connecting your rig to an antenna, you need some kind of line to link the two together. Now I remember once going to one breaker's 10-20 and finding that he had his antenna hooked up by using 2-lead speaker wire that ran 10 meters outside to an antenna mounted on a broom handle. Mercy Sakes! He was wondering why he wasn't getting out. The best thing to use to hook up your rig is coax. Coax shields your line so that only your antenna radiates. For the right impedence match, use RG-58 or RG-8. Almost all CB antennas are made to use this kind of coax. Also it's best to make your length of coax be as short as possible. That prevents resistance losses from eating away at your power output. This starts to get critical when you run 30 meters (about 100 feet) or more of coax. We recommend that you switch to RG-8 for longer distances, because the losses for the larger-diameter cable will be much less.

RG-8 coax has a larger center wire, which presents less resistance to the electrical flow than RG-58 cable. If you transmit 4 watts through 15 meters (about 50 feet) of RG-58, only about 80% of the power reaches the antenna. With RG-8, 90% would reach the antenna. If you ran 30 meters (about 100 feet) of coax, RG-58 would give you 65% of the power to the antenna, while RG-8 would deliver about 80%.

The letter A after the number coax (e.g., RG-8 A/U) means that it is a new type wire that doesn't deteriorate after years of use. This is the best kind of coax to use. There are also other numbers for coax. RG-213 A/U is the same as RG-8 A/U. Other numbers can be looked up in cable manufacturing guides.

Cutting the Coax

It's best to have your coax be one long, unbroken run from your rig to your antenna. If splices have to be made in the line, you'll want to make sure there is good electrical contact made: Use two male PL 259 coax connectors and a double female connector. Cover the complete assembly with a waterproof coax sealing compound sold by electronic supply houses in order to protect the connection from any future moisture invasion.

It is a common myth that chopping off sections of your coax will improve your SWR. While this may change your SWR reading slightly, it won't necessarily help you get out any better. The best thing to use is the shortest length of coax possible.

If the SWR is high, check all connections in the line and make sure that the antenna is the right length and has been assembled properly. Try wiggling the coax at the connector while checking the SWR to see if there is a loose connection or a short where it was soldered.

Lightning

Hanging that big old antenna out there is sure attractive to lightning and your coax can bring it right into your house, which may produce a variety of unwanted consequences, such as a light show and Roman candle effect from your rig, and the possibility of getting zapped! Lightning usually poses no danger for mobiles. However, if you operate a base station, there are a couple of preventive measures you can take. The best thing is to unplug the main plug before a lightning storm and disconnect your coax connector. Make sure your coax connector is put away from people and things that could get zapped!

There is no substitute in lightning protection for a properly grounded antenna. To ground your base antenna, attach a thick copper wire to one of the mounting bolts that clamp your base aerial to the supporting pole. The wire should be run directly from the antenna down to ground level without any sharp bends in it. A ground clamp attaches the ground end of the wire to a ground rod. This rod is made of metal and should be hammered at least 1.5 meters (5 feet) into the ground. If you haven't got a place to drive a ground rod that deep, you can bury 3 meters (10 feet) or more of the bare wire in a trench 6" deep. Ground rods, wire and clamps can be obtained through local electrical supply stores.

An alternative method of lightning protection involves the purchase of an in-line lightning arrester. It is called "in-line" because it connects right into the coaxial line between the antenna and transceiver. A thick copper wire is then run from a ground terminal on the arrester to a ground rod. The wire connecting the arrestor to the ground rod should be run in as straight a line as possible, away from other objects, with no sharp bends in it. The main problem with an arrester is that it can eventually arc out inside after suffering a number of nearby lightning hits. However, if you tend to be forgetful or might not always be around to disconnect the coax during a storm, an arrester might be an additional safeguard that could protect you and your valuable CB equipment from a potential melt-down situation.

Towers and Masts

The easiest method of mounting a base antenna is to stick it up on the roof or attach it to the side of the house. One of the most popular methods of roof mounting is accomplished by using a chimney mount, like the kind used for the installation of TV aerials. There are other kinds of roof mounts available. The choice that you make will depend on what your rooftop is like. Some things to keep in mind are:

When putting it up, make sure it's in a good position so that if something slips, the antenna can't fall on top of the main power line.

Small antennas like ground planes or three-element beams can be supported on a section of pipe or on push-up type poles with guy wires. A push-up is made of three or more sections of pipe, which telescopes up to 15 meters (50 feet) or less. The sections are held together by clamps and bolts. You attach your antenna to the top section, put the pole on the ground, and extend and clamp one section of pipe at a time, straight up. Tape your coax and any rotating cable as the pole goes up. You'll usually need a step ladder and some help from your friends.

Larger antennas, including beams, should be supported by a triangular tower. Triangular towers are available in many models. Most of them come in three-meter (10-foot) sections that bolt together. Some are free standing; they don't need guy wires or support if they are cemented into the ground. Check the manufacturer's specifications.

Before putting up a tower or any other large size antenna support system in a residential neighborhood, it is advisable to check to see if any local zoning laws prohibit that kind of structure in your area. Failure to comply with local zoning laws can

Fig. 4-12 Tower installation

result in a fine and the forced removal of the antenna system.

Make sure the tower is sturdy. You will need to sink it into concrete in the ground and in many cases use guy wires to hold it up. When using guy wires on towers with beam antennas, make sure to have them attached to the tower far enough below the beam to permit complete 360° rotation of the antenna. Use good galvanized steel wire and an "egg" type insulator spaced every 1.5 meters (5 feet) along the guy wire until the guy wire reaches about 9 meters (30 feet) down from the antenna. Past that you don't need to use insulators. This will keep the guy wires from interfering with the radiation pattern of the antenna. Also it helps if your antenna is as clear as possible from other buildings, trees, metallic objects or other large obstructions.

Another common method of supporting a tower is to mount it against one wall of a house or building. Keep in mind that your tower may be subjected to high winds and stress.

Tower construction usually involves the help of some experienced people and a *Jinn Pole*. A Jinn Pole is a stout aluminum pole with a clamp assembly on one end and a pully on the other. After sinking the tower section into the ground, the Jinn Pole is clamped to the top of that section. A heavy rope runs through the pully, which is now about 3 meters (10 feet) above the top of the bottom section. One end of the rope is tied to the middle of each new section. One or more people on the ground can pull on the other end of the rope, until

Fig. 4-13 Top of the tower

the new section is comfortably suspended over the bottom section. From there it can be easily lowered into place and bolted onto the section below. This procedure is repeated until the top section of the tower has been placed. **Always use a good safety belt whenever climbing or working on any tower.**

Rotators

A rotator is an electronic motor that allows you to turn your beam in any direction you want. TV-type rotators should only be used with the smallest of beams, those with three elements or less.

For large beams, you will need a heavy-duty rotator made especially for CB or HAM use. They come with a control box which is wired to the rotator by an electric cable. Make sure to get a cable long enough to reach from your antenna to your radio, with some to spare in case you might want to move the position of your radio sometime in the future. The rotator is usually mounted on the tower a few feet from the top. The mast should be made of thick-wall galvanized pipe 4.5 cm (1¾") in diameter or bigger.

Test your rotator on the ground before you put it up on the tower. Hook it up according to manufacturer's directions. After checking to see if it rotates in a full circle, set it on north. Then turn off the power and disconnect the leads. Before tightening the final mount bolts on the antenna, make sure that your beam is pointed in the direction of north. That way, your indicator and your antenna will match. Make sure to leave enough slack in your coax between the tower and mast to allow the antenna to rotate freely. You also need to leave a little slack on your rotator cable to prevent it from pulling on the connections. Both coax and rotator cables should be taped to one leg of the tower. These cables should not be brought away from the tower until you get at least 3 meters (10 feet) below the lowest part of the beam.

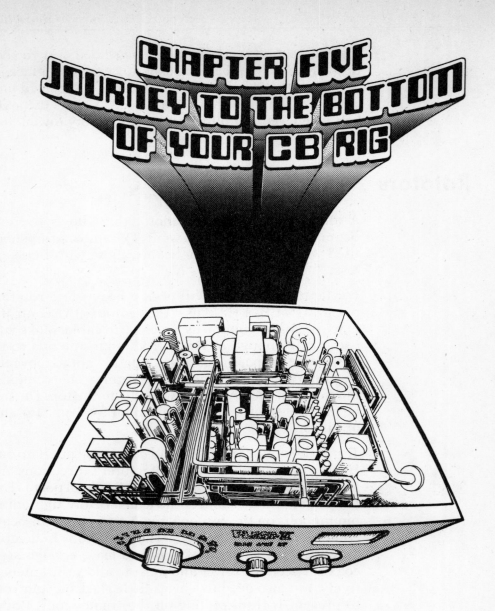

CHAPTER FIVE
JOURNEY TO THE BOTTOM OF YOUR CB RIG

Ladies and Gentlemen! May I have your attention please? It's time to embark on CB Safari's grand tour of Radio City. Through the use of an incredible patented shrinking process, we shall be able to stroll down the transmit and receive boulevards of your favorite CB radio. Please stay with the group. Although we have plenty of time set aside for this afternoon's tour, we don't intend on getting bogged down by all the details. At this point, we merely wish to give you a "ball park" view of just how any CB radio works. And be careful not to touch anything. This base station has some capacitors that carry a charge of 500 volts, enough juice to knock your socks off! Interested parties can hire one of our trail guides later on if they want to go exploring on their own.

Now if you will follow me over to the antenna, we are ready to catch the next wave and slide down into the rig. Wow. Look at that giant coil just humming with juice! Okay, now that we're all together, everyone look at their copy of the tour map for the section of Radio City known as the receiver.

Inside the CB Receiver

The radio wave that we just rode in here on has just entered a Radio Frequency Amplifier, where the signal is made a lot stronger. From less than a millionth of a volt, our signal jumps to a tenth of a volt or so.

With a forty channel rig, it's important to be able to select which channel you want to listen to and reject the others. There are filters that can be used that would only let a little slice of all the incoming radio frequencies pass on through. If this radio used filters designed to only pass one specific channel, the rig would have to have 40 individual filters to receive all the available CB channels! The cost of forty filters would be more than the price of all the other CB parts combined! Years back, however, some smart engineers figured that if they first reduced any incoming 27 MHz frequency to one standard intermediate frequency, then

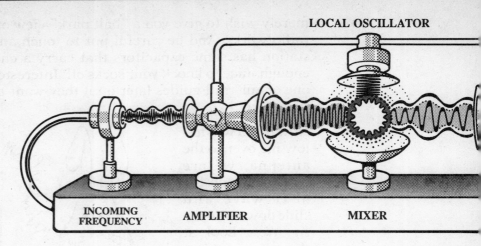

Fig. 5-1 AM CB receiver processing incoming signal

they could use the same filter for every CB channel. This frequency is about 10 million cycles per second, or Hertz. That's quite a step down from 27 million. The reason for this intermediate frequency is that it helps your receiver give clearer, more selective reception.

That's the "why" of intermediate frequency. The "how" is that we run the signal through a *mixer circuit,* where we also shoot in another high frequency signal. These two signals mix together and produce a third signal, just like mixing red and blue paint together will give you purple. This third frequency is the intermediate frequency and it contains all of the modulation that was within the original 27 MHz signal. The process of mixing two signals together in order to obtain a third is called *heterodyning.*

By the way, the second high frequency is made by a circuit called the local oscillator; local because the signal is made right in your rig as opposed to the incoming signal which comes from tens, hundreds or even thousands of miles away. It's also an oscillator because electricity inside the circuit oscillates back and forth so fast that it becomes a radio frequency.

So, now we have a much slower signal coming out of the mixer at usually 10 million Hertz. Once again we make the signal stronger by running this frequency through an I.F.(intermediate frequency) amplifier and filter, helping to select just the frequency we want.

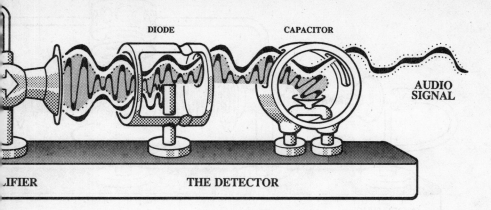

DIODE   CAPACITOR

AUDIO
SIGNAL

...LIFIER   THE DETECTOR

We're about halfway through our receiver now. If any of you want to rest, you can sit down on them resistors over there. Warm, ain't they? That's because some juice goes through them and the resistors just use juice up as heat. So, get comfortable while I tell you about the next mind boggling circuit!

North American CB Receiver Circuitry

AM CB radios like those used in the U.S. and Canada have a little beauty called a *detector* circuit. Its job is to strip the audio signal off of that I.F. frequency that we just saw amplified. The audio is contained in the I.F. frequency just like it was in the original radio signal that came in the antenna behind us. We reduced the incoming signal to an intermediate frequency, but that didn't affect the voice frequencies at all. This detector has the ability to pass all the voice energy on and discard the radio frequency energy. The radio signal brought the voice through the ozone but now that we got it, we have no further use for it.

Fig. 5-2 AM CB receiver block diagram

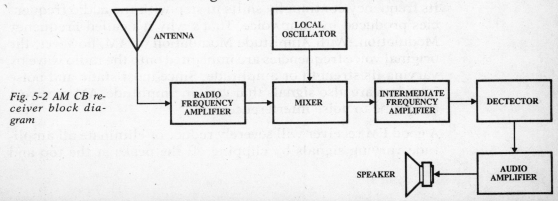

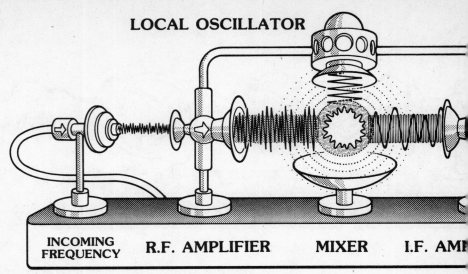

LOCAL OSCILLATOR

INCOMING FREQUENCY   **R.F. AMPLIFIER**   **MIXER**   **I.F. AMP**

Fig. 5-3 FM receiver processing incoming signal

That's why the radio frequency energy is called a *carrier* — because the voice is the information, and once it is delivered, the carrier has served its purpose. It's like when you bring home a pizza from the take-out place: it's the goodies that you're interested in, not the container.

European CB Receiver Circuitry

Unlike American CB radios which use AM, European CBs are FM units. Radio City here has the ability to process both AM and FM CB signals. If you are a European CBer or an American CBer that would like to take a CB tour of Europe someday, pay special attention to the next couple of stops on the tour. Otherwise you can skip ahead to the next station on today's route.

Although an FM radio wave is always kept at an even strength, its frequency continually shifts in step with the audio frequencies produced by your voice. That's why it's called Frequency Modulation. With Amplitude Modulation or AM, however, the original voice frequencies are imprinted onto the radio wave by varying its strength or amplitude. Since most static and noise impulses are also signals that vary in amplitude, AM receivers are prone to noise interference.

A good FM receiver will severely reduce or eliminate all amplitude varying signals by clipping off the peaks at the top and

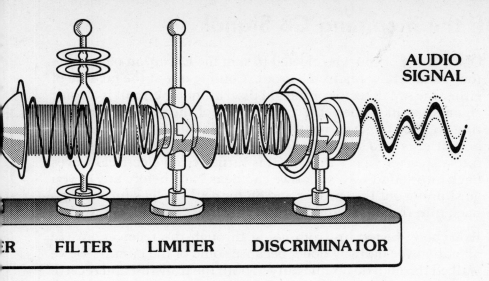

AUDIO
SIGNAL

FILTER   LIMITER   DISCRIMINATOR

bottom of the I.F. signal. And that's what this next little beauty does: it's called the FM limiter.

The next circuit on the FM part of the receiver tour is called the discriminator and its job is to take the audio signal off of the I.F. frequency after it has gone through the limiter. The audio is contained in the I.F. signal just like it was in the original radio signal that came in the antenna behind us. We reduced the incoming signal to an intermediate frequency, but that didn't affect the voice frequencies at all. The discriminator has the ability to turn the frequency shifting of the FM signal back into audio.

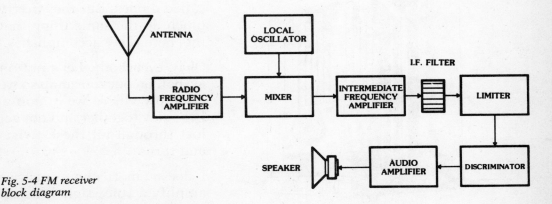

Fig. 5-4 FM receiver block diagram

Peeling Off the Incoming CB Signal

Okay. Those of you who elected to skip the European part of the tour should now rejoin the group. Coming out at the far side of either the AM detector or the FM discriminator circuit is a voice signal, just like when it left the mouth of the person transmitting to you. We then run this audio signal through an audio amplifier or two so it's comfortably loud, and then it goes right into a speaker where the signal is turned from electrical waves back into sound waves that we can hear. Now before any of you go slipping out the speaker and on to the floor, let's turn and go back into the radio, and find out how this contraption works.

Everybody rested up from going through the receiver? We're actually over halfway done, because some of the circuits we've walked through do double duty in both the transmit and receive parts of the trip.

Inside the CB Transmitter

See that big plastic container over there? That's the relay. The relay is a kind of switch which connects either the transmit or the receive circuits together. It's controlled by the push button on the microphone. That's how the parts common to both transmit and receive are switched back and forth. After all, transmitting is just receiving in reverse. Some of the latest CB radios have replaced the relay with a group of cheaper electronic parts called diodes. But they pretty much do the same thing that this here relay accomplishes.

Okay, everybody. Let's put an eyeball on our tour map so we all know where we're going. Let's stay together and not get lost through all these twists and turns.

It doesn't matter how much we amplify a voice signal, it just won't radiate off your antenna,

RELAY

it's too low a frequency. That's why we need a radio carrier, and we'll see how it's produced in a minute.

I'll have to ask you kids over there not to throw your trash all over that circuit board. Otherwise, the local sanitation worker's union will give the next tour group a hard time because of your sloppiness.

Generating Good Vibrations

If you'll look where I'm pointing, that's where CB's resident guru—the Master Crystal Oscillator—lives. Within that square tin can over there is a thin sliver of quartz crystal which vibrates, generating an electrical frequency.

A crystal is just what it says. It is a piece of quartz crystal (a rock) in a can. It operates on the same principle as a tuning fork. When you hit a tuning fork, it will vibrate at a particular frequency. The tone or frequency depends on how the tuning fork is constructed. A crystal operates in a similar way. When hit with electricity, the crystal will vibrate at a frequency, which is determined by the thickness of the crystal.

If you had to buy a crystal for every single frequency needed in a 40 channel CB, it would cost you a pretty penny. Prior to the FCC's approval of a 40-channel plan for U.S. CBers, many CB radios used a few crystals and ran the frequencies they produced through some mixing circuits to get 23 channels. But with the electronic industry's ever growing demand for quartz crystals, even this arrangement became undesirable, and the Radio City engineers came up with a totally new concept.

There is another kind of oscillator which can be tuned over a wide frequency range. It generates frequencies by means of a tuned circuit instead of a crystal. The parts inside the tuned circuit cycle electricity back and forth, vibrating at the 27 MHz carrier frequency. This oscillator's frequency can be altered by changing the voltage at one part of the tuned circuit. That's why this kind of oscillator is called a voltage controlled oscillator (VCO).

By itself, the VCO isn't stable enough to be the generator of a stable radio signal. It drifts away from its set frequency too easily—something undesirable in a radio transmitter. Fortunately, a VCO can be combined with some other circuits which help to keep it anchored onto the channels. This combination of circuits is called the Phase Lock Loop (PLL).

Inside the Phase Lock Loop

With the aid of the crystal oscillator and the VCO, the Phase Lock Loop can easily generate all 40 CB channels. Instead of more crystals, the PLL uses several inexpensive integrated circuits— by-products of the computer revolution. Each integrated circuit (or IC) is actually several transistor circuits contained in one small plastic blob.

Hey, how about one of you dudes over there going over to the channel selector and kicking us down to channel one!

The channel selector knob programs one of these IC chips to divide the crystal frequency down to a fraction of its original frequency. The Phase Lock Loop compares this signal to a sample of the VCO frequency. If the PLL senses no difference between them, then the VCO is locked onto channel one's frequency. If the VCO starts to drift off frequency, the PLL's comparator will sense the change and send a correcting voltage back into the VCO. Once back on track, the difference between the two signals disappears, and the PLL shuts off the correcting voltage. The more that the VCO has drifted off of the programmed frequency, the more voltage required to bring it back into line.

So let's flip over to channel five and see what happens. Every time that we switch channels, we are making a small, calculated change in how the master crystal frequency is divided. This unbalances the compared frequencies just enough to make the PLL readjust the VCO on up to the new channel's frequency. It will remain locked to the new channel's frequency until we spin the knob again. It is the channel selector that sends a coded message to the PLL causing this whole chain of events to occur.

Fig. 5-5 CB trans-
mitter processing
outgoing signal

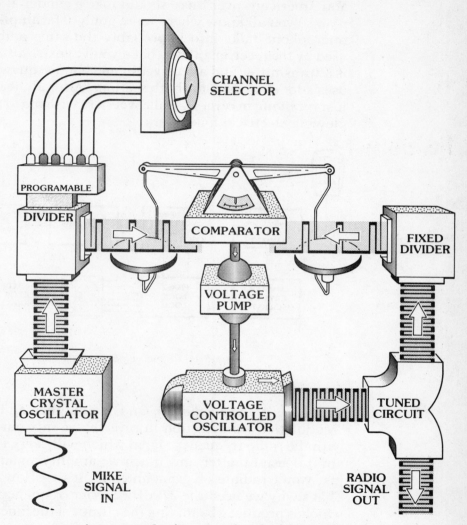

So as we've seen, this is some kind of fancy circuit. By using a crystal as a reference frequency, the PLL can make a normally finicky VCO have the frequency stability of a precision crystal!

Well folks, before we follow this VCO's 27 MHz frequency on up towards the antenna, let's take a look at how the audio signal from the microphone gets added onto that carrier frequency. Since AM CBs differ from FM CBs in this respect, we need to once again split the tour group into two parties.

Inside a North American CB Transmitter

You Americans over there should take a gander at our AM tour map so you all know where we're going. The amplifier that the microphone talks into is probably the same audio amplifier used by the receiver. I'll bet that if you've got a *transceiver*, which is a transmitter and a receiver in one handy squawkbox, that it uses a lot of circuits for both sections. After all, transmitting is just receiving in reverse. Walk over here with me to this bunch of glowing electrical machinery.

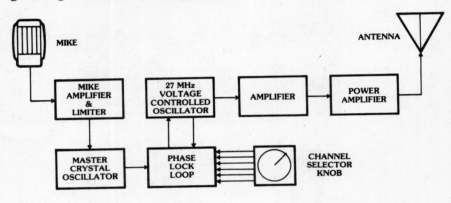

Fig. 5-6 AM CB transmitter block diagram

This here is the *modulator*, and it's another audio amplifier. "Modulation" is detection in reverse: we mix our voice signal with the radio frequency signal which will carry it out into the air. It doesn't matter how much we amplify an audio signal, it just won't radiate off your antenna, it's too low a frequency. That's why we need the 27 MHz carrier frequency. The carrier, which is produced by mixing the output of the fancy PLL circuit we saw at a couple of stops ago with the frequency produced by a second reference crystal, is first amplified from a few millionths of a volt until it is strong enough to drive the 4-watt radio frequency power amplifier. The modulator over there makes the intensity of the juice in the power amplifier change with your voice. Once the 4-watt signal has been AM-modulated, it gets kicked back out the antenna plug.

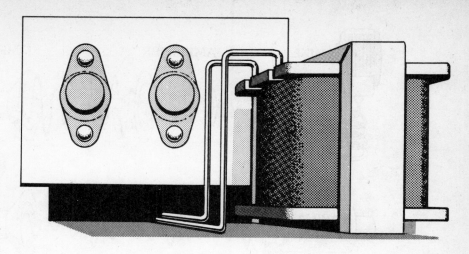

Fig. 5-7 AM modulation circuit

Inside a European CB Transmitter

Okay European party, heads up! Take a look at our FM tour map so you all know what's coming up next. Let's stay together and not get lost through all these twists and turns.

With FM CB, modulation is accomplished by varying the frequency rather than the intensity of the 27 MegaHertz CB radio wave. Although a crystal is normally a highly-stable component, it is possible to vary its frequency slightly by hooking up a capacitor to it. There is a special electronic part called a varicap

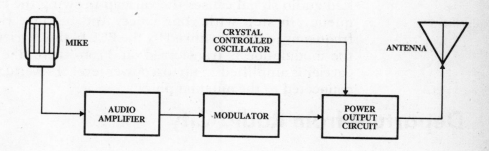

Fig. 5-8 FM transmitter block diagram

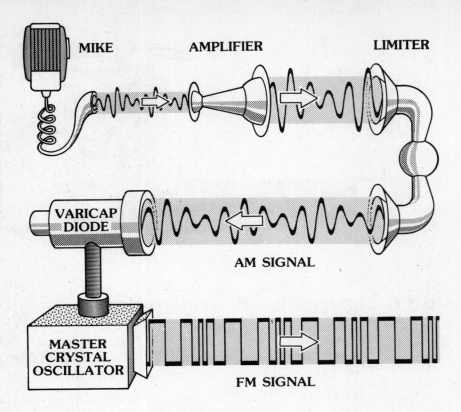

Fig. 5-9 FM modulation process

diode, and it will act like a variable capacitor when a changing voltage is applied to it. In order to get FM, the mike's audio is amplified and then hooked up to the varicap diode. The amplified audio signal causes the varicap to swing the crystal's frequency in step with your voice. And because the crystal's frequency is directly linked by the PLL to the carrier frequency, the modulation is transferred on. From there, the modulated carrier is amplified on up to a power level of several watts and is connected to the antenna plug.

Departure from Radio City

Well, here we all are again at the antenna. I hope none of this has left any of you out in the street. We've kind of gone all the way through this maze and come all the back round to the beginning. That power amplifier was the last circuit.

Now everybody get ready. We're getting out on the antenna now and we're about to leap out there into the sky. We'll radiate on out there, traveling at the speed of light for thousands of miles out into the Universe, ending up heaven knows where.

Chapter Six

AM, SSB, and FM

AM, SSB, and FM are three ways that radio waves can be altered to carry your voice. There are several differences between these three modes of communication that you should know about. While only AM and SSB are legally available in the U.S., several European governments have decided to legalize only FM CB radios. In some parts of the world, CBs capable of transmitting by means of all three modes can legally be purchased and used. Each mode has its own good and bad points. We want you to

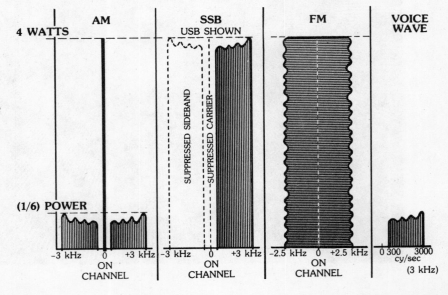

Fig. 6-1 AM/FM/SSB comparison

understand what they are and how they affect your ability to communicate.

Let's start out by examining an unmodulated radio wave or carrier. Both an AM and a FM carrier are exactly the same. It's only after the addition of your voice that the FM and AM radio waves take on their own special characteristics.

Amplitude Modulation

When a radio wave is amplitude modulated (AM), the carrier frequency never varies. It's the strength or amplitude of the carrier that is continually changing. The louder the sound reaching the mike, the greater the variation of the carrier's strength and the louder the audio will be at the receiver. The pitch or frequency of your voice controls the rate that the AM carrier varies in amplitude. If your voice is vibrating at a frequency of 1000Hz, then the strength or amplitude of the carrier will change 1000 times a second.

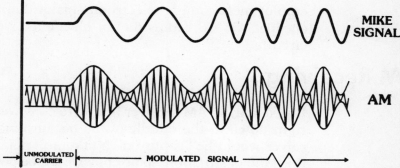

Fig. 6-2 AM modulation

The percentage of modulation is the amount of modulation riding on the carrier. One-hundred percent modulation is the heaviest change you can put the carrier through without overloading it.

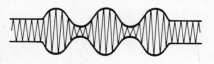

Fig. 6-3 50% and 100% modulation

50% MODULATION   **100% MODULATION**

Overmodulation

An overmodulated AM carrier is still understandable, but it will cause bleedover onto nearby channels and transmit spurious signals or harmonics which can cause interference to other radio services throughout the higher radio bands. AM CB radios are manufactured with an automatic modulation limiter which prevents most units from overmodulating. But in some situations (like when a power mike is added to the radio), overmodulation can be a problem.

AM Noise Elimination

Unlike FM, an AM receiver is constructed to respond to signals that vary in amplitude. Since most static and noise impulses are amplitude changing signals, they are received along with the CB signals. The development of effective noise blanker and automatic noise limiter circuits have done much to improve the quality of AM reception. But they require manufacturers to employ more complex electronics inside their units. Many of the cheaper AM CB radios do not have effective noise eliminator circuits.

AM Receiving

Unlike FM, an AM receiver is able to copy weak signals that are right down in the middle of the background noise. An FM receiver would be "captured" by the noise and not the signal in this kind of situation, so no copy would be possible. When more than one AM station keys up on the channel simultaneously, it is still possible to copy both stations on AM with the accompaniment of the squeals or heterodyne caused by the two signals beating together.

An AM receiver is also capable of picking up FM transmissions occuring on one of the channels, and an understandable if somewhat thin sounding copy is possible.

Single Side Band

When the mike signal and carrier are mixed together in the modulator, they form a new signal which is the composition of the two signals. The audio is both on top of and underneath the carrier frequency. These two layers of signal are called the upper and lower sidebands.

At 100% modulation of an AM carrier, two-thirds of the total power is contained in the carrier, and one-third is divided between the two sidebands. The sidebands are like mirror images and either one has all the audio signal necessary for reception. By filtering out the carrier and one of the sidebands on transmit, we can have a stronger, more compact signal. SSB transmission puts all of the power into the message. That's why an SSB signal has a gain of 9 dB over an equivalent AM signal. Switching from AM to SSB can more than double your range.

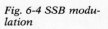
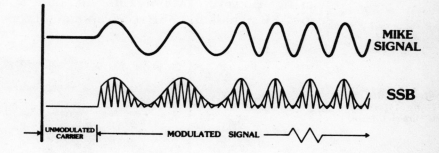

Fig. 6-4 SSB modulation

Because of the narrower bandwidth, more SSB stations can fit into the high frequencies that are shared by worldwide radio services. That's why SSB has become the preferred mode for international short-wave voice communications. In the CB band, SSB doubles the amount of channels for use, making more room for everybody. Some of the more dedicated CB operators have turned to SSB as a way to escape the "looney tune" activities which all too often descend on AM operators in crowded urban areas.

Tuning the Clarifier

In order for SSB to be received as an understandable audio signal, the missing carrier must be added back into the SSB signal at the receiving end. That is why SSB signals sound so muffled and jumbled when heard on an AM receiver. SSB receivers use an additional circuit, called the clarifier, which adds the carrier back in. By carefully tuning the clarifier, the SSB signal goes from sounding like one of the robot Cylon Warriors from *Battlestar Galactica* into an understandable and natural-sounding voice.

Because of this extra control, SSB radios are harder to operate than AM or FM CBs. For an understandable reception, you must select the correct sideband—usually the lower side band—of the station you are listening to. While the clarifier allows you to tune in to the exact receive frequency, it does not affect your outgoing signal in any way.

More natural sounding voices are possible on AM or FM, in contrast to the duck-squawking heard when using SSB. While receiving in the SSB mode it is possible to copy AM signals by "nulling out" the carrier through careful adjustment of the clarifier. However, AM-only CBs will not be able to successfully copy SSB signals and SSB receivers cannot copy FM CB signals.

Fig. 6-5 Uniden Grant AM/SSB CB (Courtesy Uniden)

SSB transmissions are totally incompatible with FM or AM signals. Whenever FM or AM and SSB signals co-inhabit the same channels, they can clobber each other, causing mutual interference.

Some SSB radios have a VOX (for voice operated transmit) control. Instead of keying the mike for every transmission, just talking into the mike will automatically key the transmitter up. During pauses between phrases or sentences the transmitter will unkey, giving the other station an opportunity to break into the conversation to make comments. A VOX-operated two-way QSO is much more like a telephone conversation than the key-down FM or AM contact is.

SSB has a greater range per watt over FM or AM and is the favorite mode among skip talkers. SSB has the ability to cut through static and noise, when an FM or AM signal wouldn't make the trip. And SSB's efficient use of the frequency space makes it more appealing for use in cities and other congested areas. But SSB requires a much more complex and expensive circuitry to compact and filter the SSB radio waves.

Fig. 6-6 Realistic AM/SSB CB mobile (Courtesy Radio Shack Div. of Tandy)

Frequency Modulation

The strength of an FM radio's signal or its power output always remains the same. What changes when we modulate the carrier is the frequency of the radio wave. The higher the tone of your voice, the more times a second that the FM carrier will swing back and forth from channel frequency. If you hummed a 1000 Hertz tone into your mike, the radio wave will change frequencies 1000 times in one second.

Deviation

The total amount of frequency change or swing from the carrier frequency is called the deviation. Legally, the maximum change allowed in the UK from the 27 MegaHertz channel frequency is ± 2.5 KiloHertz, and all FM transceivers are preset at the factory to prevent you from going over that. So if you were on channel one, or 27.60125 MHz, the carrier could swing as high as 27.60375 MHz or as low as 27.59875 MHz. If an FM transmission did deviate too much, it would exeed the FM CB receiver's

DEVIATION

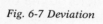

Fig. 6-7 Deviation

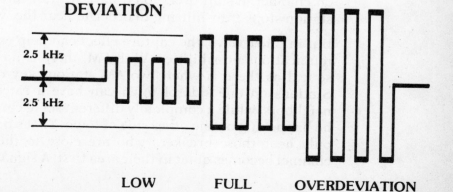

2.5 kHz

2.5 kHz

LOW   FULL   OVERDEVIATION

bandwidth and would sound distorted. It could even overlap onto the next channel, causing interference.

With FM, the louder the voice going into the mike, the greater the deviation. And the greater the deviation, the louder that the audio will be when it comes out of the receiver's speaker.

Other FM radio services are allowed to use wider deviations. Two-way radios in the VHF bands are used by police, ambulances, fire departments and other emergency services because of FM's high fidelity and solid sound. All these radios use a ±kHz deviation. FM broadcast stations use a ±75 kHz deviation. Because of the music's wider frequency range (up to 20,000 Hz), a wider deviation is necessary in order to reproduce the full spectrum of audio dynamics. But this also takes up bigger channel spaces in the radio bands. Most two-way radios are designed only to hear and transmit sound in the lower spectrum of human hearing. They won't pass sound frequencies higher than 3000 Hz. This applies to most AM and SSB radios as well.

Using a narrow deviation of ±2.5 kHz makes it possible for an FM CB signal to occupy slightly less room per channel than an AM signal would. This narrow deviation, however, sacrifices some of the signal's voice power.

The Capture Effect

One unique aspect of FM is called the "capture effect". An FM receiver will be captured by the strongest signal on channel. Any other weak breakers on channel at the time will be overridden! In some ways this limits the range of an FM signal in cities or other crowded areas where there is a lot of CB activity. If you are trying to copy a weak mobile when some strong station keys up on channel, it's all over. You'd have to wait until the stronger station stops transmitting in order to hear the weaker station.

But in other ways, the capture effect can help extend the communications possibilities. With FM, there is no heterodyne or squeal as there is when two AM stations key down together. Stations on one side of town can have a ratchet with their neighbors, while a completely different set of conversations can be happening on the other side of town. That's because stations only hear those breakers who are close to them, unless the channel becomes quiet in their area first. A signal only has to be a little stronger than the background noise in order to capture the FM receiver. When captured, an FM receiver is fully quieted—background static on the channel is no longer heard. This makes for a clean copy.

Kicking Out The Noise

Another aspect of FM is the ability of a good receiver to reject static and other noise impulses. Most noise is similar to AM in that it varies in strength rather than frequency. A good FM receiver will not respond to signals that vary in strength. Consequently, neither background noise nor AM modulation are copied on an FM receiver. Also FM receivers offer a more effective squelch control than AM radio does. Generally, if a station isn't strong enough to break the squelch, then it wouldn't be good enough for you to copy anyway. So you should keep your FM receiver squelched, eliminating background noise. Both of these noise eliminating factors put FM a notch above the normal racket that is an unavoidable part of AM SSB listening.

Once a mobile FM station gets close enough to you to fully quiet the background noise, any further addition in signal strength will make little difference in the receiver's loudness. Once you have set the volume control to a comfortable level, it is usually unnecessary to readjust it. Also FM signals will not overload an FM receiver—even if the other breaker is parked right next to you. An AM receiver's front end would become overloaded in this kind of situation, causing distortion of the received signal.

One of the main complaints made by AMers about FM CB is that they can't talk skip on FM. This is true only because most foreign DX stations do not have FM capabilities on their CB rigs. FM signals will skip however, and the quality of skip on FM is about the same as AM. Generally, FM will get out as much or more than AM, but SSB will take you even further.

Chapter Seven

DX Guide
for CBers

*So go ahead England!
You got the Momma-Mia in the pizzaria, c'mon!*

For many years, *short wave listening (SWL)* has been a popular hobby of hundreds of thousands of people throughout the world. Many folks depend on short-wave broadcast stations for news, weather and other important information. Others tune in just to copy the fascinating spectrum of activities occurring throughout the 3 to 30 MHz HF bands. It is possible to monitor ships at sea, airplanes, radio amateurs and military and government frequencies. But we think the SSB and AM skip contacts from around the globe can be as interesting as any of the above. If you want to get a copy on some of this skip action, then follow us out to DX-Land and we'll let you in on when and where to listen.

Sunspots

Violent whirlpools of ultraviolet radiation located on the surface of the sun are responsible for the frequent reception of CB stations from around the world. These solar storms are called sunspots, and the intense radiation released by them electrically charges the upper layers of the earth's atmosphere, called the *ionosphere.*

The Sunspot Cycle

Although sunspot activity has been monitored and recorded for over 200 years, it has only been associated with radio since 1901, when Marconi first bridged the Atlantic with radio waves. Scientists then theorized that sunspots created an electrically charged region in the earth's atmosphere which could reflect radio signals across the ocean.

Now we know that the number of sunspots goes up and down in an eleven-year cycle. The last peak was in 1980 and the next one should occur in 1991. We are still learning about sunspots and there may even be other, longer term cycles of solar activity that we don't know about yet. But one thing that we do know: the more sunspots there are, the more skip there is!

Fig. 7-1 Sunspot activity from 1975 to 1991 (est.)

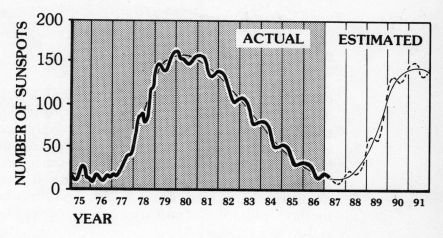

During the mid-1980's, the sunspot cycle reached its low point and a good part of the time the CB band was dead except for local communications. Then a new cycle began and the rising number of sunspots caused the skip activity to pick up again. By 1991, at the very peak of the current cycle, skip conditions will exist throughout the day. During the right times just about every part of the world will be heard!

Radio waves mainly travel in straight lines like beams of light. Although some parts of a radio wave will travel along the surface of the earth, other parts will shoot off at various angles into the sky. When a radio wave reaches the ionosphere it can bounce off of it much like a mirror reflects a beam of light. The signal is reflected back down to earth, traveling from 350 miles to several thousand miles. Sharp angles may not be reflected; consequently, there is a zone where communications is not normally possible. On other occasions, it is possible to talk into this "no skip zone".

The ionosphere is actually made up of several layers that are located anywhere from 30 to 300 miles above the surface of the

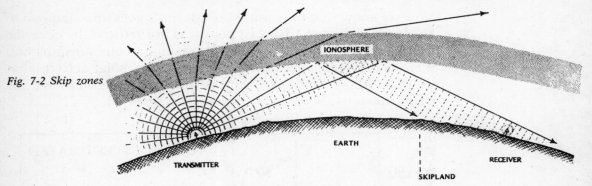

Fig. 7-2 Skip zones

earth. The height of the lowest layer at any given moment depends on the season, the time of the day and the intensity of the sun. When the layers are not very strongly charged, the radio waves may pass through and not be reflected back to earth. If it is strongly charged, the signal may bounce once, hit land or water, and bounce back skyward to be reflected again by the ionosphere. This kind of skip is called multiple hop, and by this method, radio waves can span the globe when conditions are right.

The Seasonal Skip Cycle

In addition to the eleven-year cycle, the year's seasonal changes affect the ionosphere for the same reasons that the earth's revolution around the sun affects the warmth and coolness of the earth.

Summer. During the summer months, the earth and its atmosphere reach much higher temperatures than at other times of the year. The heat causes the ionosphere to expand, lowering its overall charge intensity.

At the height of the sunspot cycle, summer provides enough

ionization to allow reflection of radio waves, although the skip distances are often not as long as at other times of the year. Since the summer nights are shorter, there is insufficient time for the ionosphere to discharge between days. So there are less intense variations in the skip throughout a 24 hour period than there are at other times of the year.

Summer during the medium to low years of the sunspot cycle is a different story altogether! The ionosphere will often be insufficiently charged for much regular skip to happen.

Winter. During winter months, the cooler atmospheric temperatures cause the ionosphere to contract, which gives it a more intense charge. This causes excellent long distance skip during the day. January and February are the best months in the Northern Hemisphere for DXing. The skip is often very long, with band openings to particularly far away areas occurring reliably every day.

The longer winter nights give the ionosphere plenty of time to discharge between the periods of daylight. Consequently, the nighttime skip is much more unreliable than in summer, with frequent periods of low skip activity that can last for days or weeks on end.

Spring and Fall. These are transitional periods, with the early spring and late fall exhibiting a tendency toward the winter condition and the late spring and early fall somewhat closer to the summer conditions. During this period, October and November are the best months for DX.

The Daily Skip Cycle

As each day rolls on, different parts of the world will become accessible for DX contacts. Often the skip is at its best when the sun is about halfway between you and the area you want to listen for. This is because the sun has sufficiently charged the ionosphere between the two stations. You will usually hear skip from the east in the morning, and from the west in the afternoon. North/South skip can happen at any time of the day. Around the times of sunrise and sunset the skip is often the longest. The following chart should give you a general idea of when to listen to your favorite foreign station. But remember that skip conditions are not totally predictable by any means.

Even during the low point of the sunspot cycle there can be isolated peaks of skip activity that open up without warning!

Predawn. Skip openings occur sporadically until shortly before sunrise.

Sunrise. At this time the sun has charged the ionosphere for thousands of miles to the east, making it possible to have very long skip in that direction until mid-morning or so.

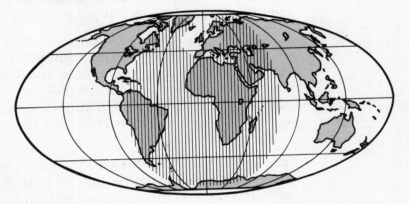

Fig. 7-3 Early morning skip for the East Coast of the US

Mid-Morning. Skip to the east becomes somewhat shorter and North/South contacts are possible.

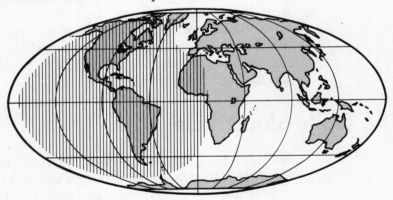

Fig. 7-4 Mid-day skip conditions allows CB signals from both East and West Coasts to be received

Midday. With the sun overhead, skip contacts in all directions are likely. This is a good time for skip of 800 miles or less. Usually the very long skip to the east has tapered off by now.

Late Afternoon. Longer skip into the west begins now. Skip from the east drops off, but North/South path is still open.

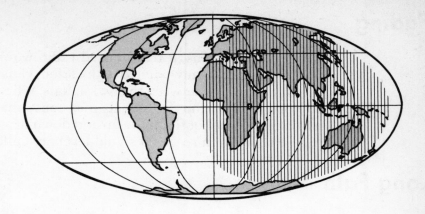

Fig. 7-5 By late evening the skip zone has moved over the Pacific Ocean region.

Sunset. At sunset skip to the west can be open for very long distances. North/South contacts are still likely.

Evening. During most of the year, skip conditions taper off within an hour or two after sunset.

Solar Storms and Radio Blackouts

Solar flares are magnetic disturbances on the surface of the sun which sometimes accompany heavy sunspot activity. Solar flares emit streams of sub-atomic particles that can totally disrupt most High Frequency (HF) skip for periods ranging from a few hours to several days long. These particles reduce the ionosphere's ability to reflect radio waves. As these particles bombard the earth they are attracted to the north and south magnetic poles. Their passage through the high polar atmosphere can actually ignite the gases there, creating aurora displays.

As the sun rotates, so does the storm and eventually it disappears to the other side which faces away from the earth, allowing normal conditions to return. But 27 days after the radio blackout first occurred the storm can reappear again from the other side of the sun and once more exert its devastating effect on CB as well as other HF skip communications.

Fading

On some occasions, a transmitted radio wave may take more than one path to any particular location, causing there to be a slight time delay between the two signals. When they recombine in your receiver the two signals may cause the reception to get stronger, weaker or fluctuate up and down in an erratic manner. These changes in received signal level are called fading.

Long Path

On many occasions, the shortest physical distance between two stations may not be the actual path that a radio wave takes when skipping. *Long Path Skip* occurs on a section of ionosphere that stretches the long way around the earth. *Long Path* openings between Europe and Australia, New Zealand, and the South

Fig. 7-6 Long path skip

Pacific, for example, happen frequently and usually occur at different times of the day than the regular openings do. DX stations with beam antennas must keep this in mind, because it can be quite critical if a beam is pointed in the opposite direction during a long path opening!

North/South Skip

Sections of ionosphere over the equator and the surrounding regions tend to get a higher charge than do other areas. This provides a path for DX contacts between the earth's Northern and Southern Hemispheres, even when skip is impossible in other directions. During the low sunspot years most skip will be possible in the southern hemisphere rather than east/west. North/South skip is also more common during the summer months. Listeners in North America or Europe will tend to hear a lot of South American and African stations within this period. (Habla Espanol, amigo?)

Sporadic E and Other Exotic Skip

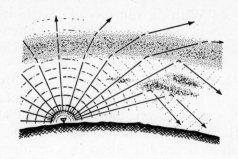

Fig. 7-7 Sporadic E skip

Sporadic E Skip is caused by irregular, low-layered clouds of ionized air. The phenomenon occurs most often in the late Spring and Summer months. There can be a small fast moving cloud reflecting radio waves from one isolated location to another or there can be large clouds covering hundreds of kilometers which can provide multiple hop skip. Sporadic E occurs frequently in the mid-morning and late afternoon, although it can occur at any time of the day. During the low part of the sunspot cycle, there are periods of time when this is the only kind of skip happening on 27 MHz.

Aurora Skip happens when signals can be reflected off the aurora borealis (or aurora australis). Aurora is usually accompanied by visual displays but there can also be radio aurora without a visual display. Sometimes auroras cause polar blackouts and radio communications over the poles fade out. When conditions are favorable, you can point your beam antenna north and hear other stations by banking off of the aurora borealis.

Back Scatter can happen anytime of the year. All the stations just point their beams south and their signals bounce off ionized clouds near the equator. With an almost direct ricochet, you can talk to nearby stations which would normally not be open to you. Your signal may split off (side scatter) at a greater angle, providing communication for a longer distance than usual. This usually results in weaker signal levels, so usually only stations with beams would scatter.

Heat Inversion usually happens in the summer, when hot and cool layers of air collide, creating an electrical charge between the layers. This static charge can cause long ground waves. It is usually noticed at night when the rest of the skip disappears. When this occurs, a radio wave can travel around the curvature of the earth, spanning greater than normal distances on the ground waves.

Kickers

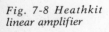

With the number of CB radios in use today, there's lots of people transmitting on all the CB channels at the same time. So when the skip rolls in, usually there's a lot of noise that comes from so many stations being on the air at once. The squeals, whistles and bumble-bees you hear on AM when two or more stations are transmitting on the same channel at once are called *heterodyne*. The only way to be heard above the heterodyne is to get louder than the rest of the stations. Most operators that you hear will be using very large antennas and illegal power amplifiers (linears, kickers, afterburners, etc.). Linears are hooked in the coaxial line between the radio and the antenna. Most of the mobile kickers are all solid state and operate off of 13.8 volts DC. Depending on the model, these units produce from 30 to 300 watts. Base amplifiers run off of 120 or 240 volt AC mains and can be tube (valve) or transistor units. The higher power base units (up to a kilowatt or two) are usually tube units. The use of power amplifiers increases the strength of a DXer's signal. It also increases the amount of interference given to other radio services and nearby electronic equipment.

Fig. 7-8 Heathkit linear amplifier

The Eleven Meter Band

In most of the world, the skip talkers use extra frequencies besides the regular 40 American channels. There is so much noise from the millions of CB users worldwide, that only the most powerful stations can work skip on the regular AM channels. Many of the skip talkers operate above, below or even in between these channels. In the U.S. and elsewhere, these operators are called Outbanders, and many of them are using sliders, VFOs or even converted Ham Radios. With this kind of equipment, outlaw CB DX operators can move freely throughout the 11 Meter Band.

Fig. 7-9 Eleven meter band

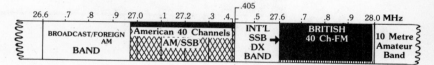

Various national government telecommunications authorities in Europe have legalized FM CB on frequencies up above the U.S. 40 channels, to prevent American and other foreign skip from taking over their local CB channels. Unfortunately, the new frequencies that were chosen have been used for years by thousands of SSB DX stations around the world. It's only a matter of time before some of those stations start talking on FM, especially when they can start hearing all the European breakers skipping in!

QSL Cards

Many DX stations have cards that they send to one another to confirm their radio contacts. These cards are called wallpaper or QSL cards. The information usually contained on these cards include: the operator's call numbers or handle, name and address, time and frequency of contact, a signal report that describes the copy, and type of radio and antenna in use. Many QSL cards are personalized with artwork and sayings that pertain to the particular station. If you hear someone coming in good from DX Land, jot down their address and drop them a line. Most folks are glad to know they are getting out and they'll send you back a card. Short Wave Listeners have been doing this for years, getting QSL cards from foreign broadcast stations.

There are stations all over the world operating AM, FM and SSB on the 40 American Channel frequencies. It is important to use the channels designated for your particular mode in order to keep from clobbering stations using other modes. Also certain channels are used for specific purposes internationally including 9, 11, 16 and 19. Channel 11 is used as the AM breaking channel in many parts of Europe. For example, it is the AM

International 40 Channel Band Plan			
Channel	**Use**	**Channel**	**Use**
1, 2, 3	FM	20,	21 open
4, 5, 6, 7	open	22, 23, 24	open
8	guard	25, 26, 27	calling
9	emergency	28, 29	AM only
10	guard	30	SSB calling
11	breaking	31, 32	open
12,	13 open	33, 34	FM
14	breaking	35	FM breaking
15	open	36	SSB calling
16	SSB only		(usually LSB)
	(usually LSB)	37	FM calling
17	calling	38	SSB calling only
18	open	39	SSB only
19	travelers	40	open

breaking channel throughout the Republic of Ireland. Channel 14 is the AM breaking channel in London as well as some other areas of the UK. Channel 16 is used in most parts of the world as the SSB breaking channel. Usually you can find many stations on this breaking channel trying to talk to foreign SSB operators.

Guard Channels should be kept free as much as possible to prevent bleedover interference onto Channel 9, the international Emergency Channel. Calling channels are used by CB clubs and other groups as a means of staying in touch with fellow members. Channel 38 is an international SSB calling channel.

SSB Lingo

> **CQ,CQ, calling CQ DX and beaming North America, this is Zulu Lima four-oh-six, in South Auckland, New Zealand calling CQ DX and standing by.**
>
> *Zulu Lima four-oh-six, this is Echo Bravo three-seven-niner in southern Ireland. Do you copy? Over!*
>
> **Roger Roger. Echo Bravo three-seven-niner, we have a five by nine copy on you this afternoon in New Zealand! The personal on this end is Mike, and my QTH is 15 kilometres southeast of Auckland, over.**
>
> *Roger Mike! Excellent copy on you here. You are five by nine plus twenty. The handle here is Richard and we are running a Yaesu FT-101 Double E here in to a five element Long John Antenna. So back to you Mike and we'll see how conditions are holding up. Zulu Lima four-oh-six, this is Echo Bravo three-seven-niner, standing by.*

SSB DX operators talk a whole other language than the AM CBers. Instead of using handles and CB lingo, SSB operators talk in a way similar to radio amateurs. They use SSB club call signs and their personal name instead of a handle. SSB operators also use the internationally-accepted Q-signal code, instead of the 10 code. The Q-code was originally developed by radio telegraphers as a kind of radio shorthand to save time when sending lengthy messages via Morse code. This practice has carried over into use by radio amateurs and SSB CB operators. A list of the more common Q-signals appears below:

QRA	Name or handle	QRX	Call back later, stand by
QRE	Estimated time of arrival	QRZ	Who is calling me?
QRG	Exact frequency	QSA	Readibility
QRH	Frequency varies (FMing)	QSB	Fading signal
QRL	Busy	QSL	Acknowledge receipt
QRM	Interference from other stations	QSM	Repeat a message
QRN	Natural interference-static	QSO	Communications with, contact
QRO	High power	QSP	I will relay to ___
QRP	Low power	QSX	Listening on the channel
QRQ	Transmit faster	QSY	Change frequency
QRS	Transmit more slowly	QSZ	Send each word of sentence more than once
QRT	Stop transmitting	QTH	Locations
QRU	I have nothing for you	QTR	Correct time is ___
QRV	I am ready		

Newcomers to SSB are advised to learn how to exclusively use SSB terminology instead of AM or FM slang if they want to blend in and be accepted as SSB operators. Mixing SSB and AM lingo is considered poor radio etiquette by dedicated SSB operators.

CQ is another old-time radio expression that lets other radio operators know that you are looking for a contact. CQ DX means that you are looking for skip and not local contacts. Single sideband operators usually talk about the frequency rather than the channel that they may be on and they tend to avoid using CB lingo or jargon in their conversations.

Readability and Signal Strength Reports

Besides swapping QSL cards, SSB DX operators usually wish to exchange signal reports. This is done by using the R-S Report Code that has been in use for many years by HAMS and commercial radio operators.

R-S Reports

Example: Your signal is coming in 5 by 9 here.

Readability

1 - Unreadable
2 - Barely readable
3 - Readable with difficulty
4 - Readable with a little
   difficulty
5 - Perfectly readable

+10 S-meter
+20 Levels
+40 over s 9 (in decibels)

Signal Strength

1 - Barely perceptible
2 - Very weak signal
3 - Weak signal
4 - Fair signal
5 - Fairly good signal
6 - Good signal
7 - Moderately strong signal
8 - Strong signal
9 - Extremely strong signal

Phonetic Alphabet

Another aid to the exchange of information via radio is the phonetic alphabet. Sometimes a station will want to get his name or address through to another operator when conditions change for the worse. Perhaps he wants a QSL card from some breaker on the other side of the world! By spelling the words phonetically, he can increase his chances of getting through the QRM and QRN. For example, Chicago, USA would be sent as "CHARLIE–HOTEL–INDIA–CHARLIE–ALPHA–GOLF–OS-CAR, UNIFORM–SIERRA–ALPHA."

International Phonetic Alphabet

ALPHA	HOTEL	OSCAR	UNIFORM
BRAVO	INDIA	PAPA	VICTOR
CHARLIE	JULIET	QUEBEC	WHISKEY
DELTA	KILO	ROMEO	X-RAY
ECHO	LIMA	SIERRA	YANKEE
FOXTROT	MEXICO	TANGO	ZULU
GOLF	NOVEMBER		

There are other phonetic alphabets you can use. You can use any words to spell out a message as long as they get the message through. Many DXers use country names like N-Norway; M-Mexico; J-Japan, etc.

Amateur Radio

During the lean years of the eleven-year sunspot cycle, favorable DX conditions on 27 MHz only occur sporadically. If you really want to talk skip, consider getting an Amateur Radio License. Amateurs are permitted to run up to 1000 (150 in the U.K. and Ireland) watts of power with no limbs or restrictions on antennas. Also, wider and less-crowded bands of frequencies are available to radio amateurs (also called Hams), each one with its own unique characteristics. After all, CB is only one tiny niche in the Electromagnetic Spectrum.

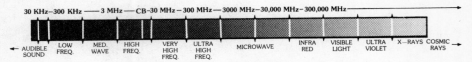

Fig. 7-10 Electromagnetic spectrum

Ham radio operators can communicate via AM, SSB, FM, telegraphy, radioteletype, facsimile and even television. There are also satellites that orbit the earth and act as automatic radio relay stations, so that Hams can talk to the other side of the world, even when the skip is down. In times of natural disaster, amateurs have often provided essential communications that have saved lives. And their electronic inventiveness has resulted in technological breakthroughs that have changed the course of modern telecommunications.

In the U.S., there are several Amateur radio licenses available. Each class has its own frequency assignments and privileges:

The *Novice* license permits High Frequency (HF) operations on several high frequency (HF) bands via Morse code. As of March 21, 1987, the FCC is also allowing Novices to transmit single sideband voice communications within the 28.300 to 28.500 MHz range, a band of frequencies not too far above the existing CB radio channels. A second section of the ten-meter Amateur radio band (28.100 to 28.300 MHz) has also been opened to Novices that wish to experiment with radio teletype (RTTY) or packet radio. SSB or FM voice operations and even two-way TV transmissions can also be conducted by Novices within the 222.01 to 223.91 MHz and 1270 to 1295 MHz spectrums. The main disadvantage of being a Novice is that you are restricted to operating within relatively narrow bands of frequencies. Novice applicants must pass an elementary radio theory examination and copy a minimum of 5 words per minute of Morse code in order to obtain a license.

While the *Technician* license requires no Morse code examination, HF voice communications are restricted to within the same 28.300 to 28.500 MHz range now available to Novices, or the VHF and UHF amateur frequency bands. Like the Novice, the technician must also pass an elementary radio theory examination that also includes questions concerning FCC rules and regulations.

Fig. 7-11 Amateur HF bands

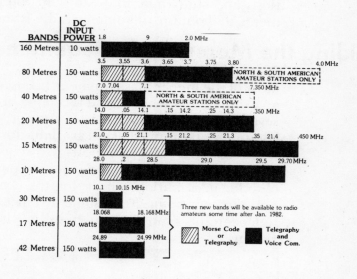

The *General* license permits HF, VHF and UHF operations via Morse code, AM, FM, and SSB as well as exotic modes like Slow Scan television (SSTV) and radio teletype (RTTY). To obtain a General license, the applicant must be able to copy Morse code at a rate of 13 words per minute and pass an examination dealing with general radio theory and FCC rules and regulations.

The *Advanced* license gives the operator access to additional frequencies in the HF bands. To obtain this class of license, the applicant must already have passed the General class Morse code and radio theory exams as well as a more advanced radio theory test.

The *Extra Class* license is the top Amateur radio license in the US. Holders of this license have complete access to all HF, VHF and UHF frequencies assigned to the Amateur radio service. To qualify for the Extra Class exam, you must have already passed the General and Advanced examinations, copy Morse code at a speed of 20 words per minute and successfully complete a written examination dealing with the more complex aspects of Amateur radio theory, operating procedures and FCC rules and regulations.

For further information on US Amateur Radio activities you can contact the American Radio Relay League, Newington, CT 06111. This non-profit organization has a number of publications and study aids that can help you pass the FCC requirements and obtain an amateur radio license of your own.

Tackling the Morse Code Requirement

Most of the higher-class Amateur licenses require that you pass an exam on the sending and receiving of Morse code. There are several excellent code practice records, tapes, and even home computer programs that are available for beginners. In the U.S., Amateur Radio examinations are scheduled periodically in most major cities. You can contact your local Amateur radio club for information concerning the nearest FCC examination point to your home 20. In some instances, licensed Radio Amateur examiners can give you the exam whenever you are ready to take it!

International Morse Code

A	di-dah	.-	Q	dah-dah-di-dah	--.-
B	dah-di-di-dit	-...	R	di-dah-dit	.-.
C	dah-di-dah-dit	-.-.	S	di-di-dit	...
D	dah-di-dit	-..	T	dah	-
E	dit	.	U	di-di-dah	..-
F	di-di-dah-dit	..-.	V	di-di-di-dah	...-
G	dah-dah-dit	--.	W	di-dah-dah	.--
H	di-di-di-dit	....	X	dah-di-di-dah	-..-
I	di-dit	..	Y	dah-di-dah-dah	-.--
J	di-dah-dah-dah	.---	Z	dah-dah-di-dit	--..
K	dah-di-dah	-.-			
L	di-dah-di-dit	.-..	.	di-dah-di-dah-di-dah	.-.-.-
M	dah-dah	--	?	di-di-dah-dah-di-dit	..--..
N	dah-dit	-.	,	dah-dah-di-di-dah-dah	--..--
O	dah-dah-dah	---			
P	di-dah-dah-dit	.--.	error	di-di-di-di-di-dit	......
1	di-dah-dah-dah-dah	.----	6	dah-di-di-di-di	-....
2	di-di-dah-dah-dah	..---	7	dah-dah-di-di-di	--...
3	di-di-di-dah-dah	...--	8	dah-dah-dah-di-di	---..
4	di-di-di-di-dah	....-	9	dah-dah-dah-dah-dit	----.
5	di-di-di-di-di	.....	0	dah-dah-dah-dah-dah	-----

Amateur Radio in the United Kingdom

The rules concerning Amateur radio operations outside of the US vary from country to country. In Great Britain, for example, any citizen over 14 years of age can qualify for a Ham Ticket. There are two classes of radio licenses available. The *Class A* license gives the holder full privileges on the HF DX Bands as well as all other amateur frequencies. The *Class B* license allows voice operation only on frequencies above 144 MHz. Both licenses require that you pass a multiple choice exam that tests your understanding of elementary radio theory, radio operating procedures, and UK rules and regulations. Hams are expected to know enough to operate a high-powered station safely and keep from transmitting signals that could interfere with other radio services. Home Office rules and regulations are based on international agreements made in Geneva thirty-five years ago.

The Radio Amateur's Exam (RAE) is given twice a year, in the spring and the autumn. Applications must be submitted three months in advance. In the United Kingdom, the Morse code exam is given throughout the year in London at the Post Office Headquarters, at all Post Office Coast Stations, or any of the Marine Radio Surveyors Offices around the country. For more information, you can write the Home Office for a free copy of their booklet, *How to Become a Radio Amateur.* In the Republic of Ireland, information on the Eire Amateur Radio Service may be obtained by writing the Radio Branch at the GPO in Dublin, Eire.

Tuning into the Action

One of the best ways to learn about Amateur Radio is get a Short Wave Receiver, so that you can actually tune into the action! With a receiver, you can listen to Morse code transmissions on the Amateur Bands. That will help develop your receiving speed. You can become familiar with amateur operating practices, frequencies of operation, and the different skip characteristics of each HF band—all aspects of radio upon which you will be tested! It takes a few months of dedicated practice and study to pass the tests, but it's worth it.

Just remember, the amateur bands are
the gateway to instantaneous planetary communications.

Chapter Eight

Gizmos

Power Mikes and Speech Compressors

A power mike has a built-in amplifier. Most of them have a volume control built into the case that you can adjust according to how loud you talk. Power mikes usually come as optional equipment and need to have a connector wired onto the cord to fit the radio.

Fig. 8-1 CB power mike

Power mikes are quite popular in the U.S. and elsewhere because they can increase the modulation or loudness of almost any AM CB. AM transceivers have a built-in circuit that limits the modulation to under 100%. Most power mikes use a crystal-type microphone element which has certain audio qualities that tend to "cut through" better than regular dynamic microphones. They usually run on a small battery inside the microphone, which lasts from six months to a year.

A power mike cannot increase the power of your transmitter above its 5-watt rating. It only adds more "punch" to your voice. When using a power mike you should get an on-the-air check to see how it sounds and adjust the volume control for the best sound while someone is listening to you. If you turn it up too high your voice will sound fuzzy, or you may get reports of squealing or breaking up.

Power mikes are available in base or mobile types, with 2 or 3 transistor preamplifiers. Usually 2 transistor preamplifiers are sufficient to modulate any transmitter. When purchasing a power mike, remember to also get a connector to fit the radio. The connector will need to be soldered on the end of the power mike's cord to match your particular transceiver. Power microphone manufacturers print pamphlets that include the wiring diagrams for almost all commercial transceivers. Make sure to check the pamphlet before purchasing a microphone to see if it is compatible with your transceiver.

A power mike usually would not increase the deviation of an FM transceiver. The mike that comes with your FM set is selected to provide all the necessary deviation. Adding a power mike might improve the audio quality of your transmission but could also result in distortion to your voice if set too high.

A speech compressor (sometimes called a range booster) is a kind of gizmo that you plug your microphone into. Some mikes are available that even contain a compressor circuit. Speech compressors are particularly effective on SSB. They boost up your voice when you talk softly and cut it down when you are talking loudly. This will raise the average power output of most SSB tranceivers. If adjusted properly, they will cut down on overmodulation and pack more punch into the signal. FM CBs usually have a compressor circuit already built into the set. So the addition of this kind of mike amplifier would not make a whole lot of difference, unless you are an unusually quiet talker.

Fig. 8-2 Icom IC-R71A shortwave receiver (Courtesy Icom America)

Short Wave Receivers

A good short-wave receiver can bring you directly into contact with the entire world of High Frequency DX, including CB, Amateur, Maritime, Aeronautical and Broadcast stations. There is no better way to learn about radio than to start experiencing it directly.

There are a wide range of models available today. When purchasing a short-wave receiver, there are a few things to look out for:

Sensitivity. Good sensitivity will extend the range of your listening. Most rigs have adequate sensitivity. But any unit's ability to pull out weak signals can be improved by the addition of an outdoor aerial. An **External Antenna Jack** allows you to plug one in. Even a random length of wire stuck up in a neighboring tree will make a tremendous difference in what you can hear.

BFO Knob or Clarifier. Many of the cheaper SW sets are made to receive AM signals only. A **Beat Frequency Oscillator** mixes an extra signal into the receiver, which lets it tune into SSB and Morse code. The duck squawk of SSB is made intelligible by fine tuning this knob. Usually it takes some practice on the part of the beginner to coordinate the dual adjustments of the main tuning knob and the BFO for adequate SSB reception.

Digital Readout. Many of the new receivers have a numerical readout of the exact frequency you are listening to. This is a big help, especially for the beginner, when you need to locate a specific frequency. It's worth the extra expense for sure.

Retractable Antenna and Battery Operation. These two features allow you to take the rig with you wherever you go. Then you can squeeze in that extra hour of Morse code practice or DX chasing wherever and whenever it becomes available.

Stability. This measures a receiver's ability to stay on the frequency selected. Check this by tuning in on a particular station. Listen for several minutes to see if the receiver drifts away from the station's frequency. Most receivers will display some degree of this when initially switched on. But after several minutes of warm-up, a good receiver will not drift.

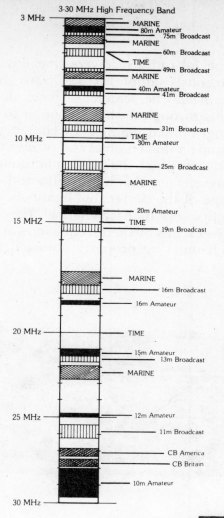

3-30 MHz High Frequency Band

3 MHz — MARINE
80m Amateur
75m Broadcast
MARINE
60m Broadcast
TIME
49m Broadcast
MARINE
40m Amateur
41m Broadcast

MARINE
31m Broadcast
10 MHz — TIME
30m Amateur

25m Broadcast
MARINE

20m Amateur
15 MHZ — TIME
19m Broadcast

MARINE
16m Broadcast

16m Amateur

20 MHz — TIME

15m Amateur
13m Broadcast
MARINE

25 MHz — 12m Amateur

11m Broadcast

CB America
CB Britain

10m Amateur

30 MHz —

*Fig. 8-3 High fre-
quency band*

Also check to make sure that when exposed to physical vibrations or shock, the frequency does not wobble or vary—an important test for any receiver with variable tuning.

Selectable Filter. Many good rigs have filters that can be adjusted to narrow the received bandwidth to just the right size, rejecting unwanted signals on nearby frequencies. This is particularly useful for picking SSB and Morse code signals out of the QRM.

Short Wave Bands. Some SW receivers do not cover the entire 3-30 MHz Band, while others may cover this as well as other additional broadcast bands above and below the HF frequencies. Aspiring CB DX listeners should make sure that the 26-30 MHz frequencies are included on any radio they buy.

Fig. 8-4 Uniden Bearcat 210XLT scanner (Courtesy Uniden)

Scanners

Scanners are special radio receivers that have the ability to almost instantaneously sample up to 20, 50 or even one hundred preselected channels. The scanner listener does not have to spend time tuning through the band in order to find the action. Once any preprogrammed channel is occupied, the scanner will automatically stop on that channel and receive the signal. Once the conversation is finished, the scanner automatically resumes sampling the preselected channels until another radio station begins to use one of the designated channels. Some scanners have a line of lights—one for each channel. They blink in succession as the receiver scans by their frequencies. All scanners have a squelch which must be properly adjusted for scanning to occur.

Fig. 8-5 Icom IC-R7000 scanning receiver (Courtesy Icon America)

A scanner can cover one or more bands of frequencies for monitoring. Some of them even cover the CB channels, as well as the VHF and UHF bands. Scanners lock onto the signal's carrier. That's why they are perfect for FM reception, but are not built for SSB which has no carrier and needs tuning for an understandable copy.

A scanner is capable of receiving a wide spectrum of local activities, including amateur, police, fire, medical, aeronauti-

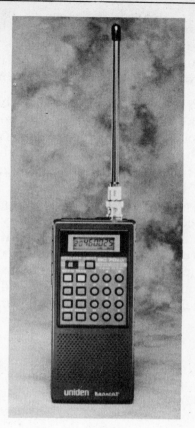

Fig. 8-6 Uniden
Bearcat BC
70XLT hand-
held scanner
(Courtesy
Uniden)

cal, marine, government, utilities and business. Scanners have become very popular recently. Be forewarned that many national telecommunications authorities frown upon the casual monitoring of most of these services as a form of entertainment. That's because some of these communications are supposed to be private and their secrecy is protected by law. However, it is legal to monitor amateur radio contacts, and if you are involved in boating, flying or services that are dispatched via radio, monitoring capabilities could be an essential aid. Operators and listeners should be aware that disclosure of overheard radio telephone and other two-way conversations to other parties is illegal.

There are two basic kinds of scanners: those that are *crystal-controlled*, and those that are *programmable*. With a crystal-controlled scanner, it is necessary to purchase a crystal for every desired channel. You must know the exact frequency for each channel before ordering crystals. This limits the capabilities of the scanner to just those frequencies that you had the foresight to order. However, the simplicity of these units allows manufacturers to miniaturize them. There are pocket scanners that fit into the palm of your hand and allow you to keep on listening, even while on the go.

Programmable scanners come with a keyboard which gives the operator a way to "enter in" any channel frequency that falls inside the scanner's tuning range. With a programmable scanner's search feature you can sweep through whole segments of a desired VHF or UHF band in a series of 5-, 10-, or 15-kHz steps. The scanner will stop on every occupied frequency. Once you've found an interesting one, just punch it into the scanner's memory. The digital frequency display reads out every frequency that you discover. Because of these extra capabilities over a crystal scanner, the programmable scanner is also more expensive. But if versatility is what you need, you'll get it by buying one of these.

There are some other features which are usually contained in either kind of scanner. A lockout feature will let you temporarily remove one or more channels from the scanner's coverage. This is useful if you want to bypass a busy channel that keeps stopping the scanner. A priority feature lets you designate one channel so that if any action occurs there the scanner will automatically revert to it, rather than continuing to be hung up on one of the other occupied frequencies. Many scanners will run off of both 12 Volts DC and 120 or 240 Volts AC so that either mobile or base operation is possible. Although a telescoping antenna is usually included for all scanners, the addition of an external monitoring antenna is essential for good mobile operation, and gives a much greater range to a base installation.

Walkie-Talkies

Fig. 8-7 Realistic TRC-216 40-channel walkie talkie (Courtesy Radio Shack Div. of Tandy)

Walkie-talkies have a variety of uses, depending on the requirements of the user and the power of the walkie-talkie itself. Some of the smaller and cheaper ones of the 100-milliwatt variety (or less) are sold as toys or for use at very close range. These are usually limited to a couple city blocks at the very most. Because their receivers are not very selective, they will pick up just about any CB radio nearby, even if it doesn't happen to be on the same channel. If you take the time to look, however, you can also find better units available in the 100-milliwatt range (no license needed). Some of them come with two or more channels. Most of these are more selective and have a cleaner sound that the cheaper toys.

The next class of walkie-talkies is in the 250-milliwatt to 2-watt class. These are usually good for communications on a clear channel up to about a couple of miles at the most. They can be used for communication to a 4-watt mobile unit. Usually this kind of walkie-talkie comes with one or two sets of crystals, and if you want any more channels than that, you have to get a set of crystals for each channel. They are usually powered by eight or ten penlight (AA) baterries. It's best to use alkaline, mercury, or re-chargable batteries, because regular batteries will run out quickly if you do a lot of transmitting.

Three to four-watt walkie-talkies are good for communications up to about five miles, maybe more, on a clear channel. There are even 40 channel units available. Some of them have the kind of features you would expect in a good mobile unit: external antenna plug, P.A., earphone, and microphone plugs, squelch, signal meter, LED channel readout, etc.

Almost all CB walkie-talkies come with telescoping antennas, most of them about 5 feet (1.5 meters) long. When using one of these, you should remember to always have the antenna extended to its full length before transmitting. This is because the SWR will be too high when the antenna is down. There are add-on antennas that can be clamped to the stub of the telescoping antenna. These are usually short springy whips about a foot or two long with a loading coil in the base. These add-on antennas

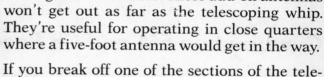

won't get out as far as the telescoping whip. They're useful for operating in close quarters where a five-foot antenna would get in the way.

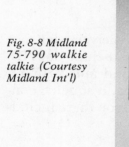

Fig. 8-8 Midland 75-790 walkie talkie (Courtesy Midland Int'l)

If you break off one of the sections of the telescoping whip, about all you can do is replace the whole whip. This is easily done. There's just one screw holding it in at the base of the whip inside the walkie-talkie. Keep the insulating grommet in place when you put the new whip in. This will prevent it from shorting out to the case of the walkie-talkie.

For really dependable service, a four-watt handheld unit with a metal case is about the best for all-around use. If you're a dedicated CBer who doesn't want to be without ears, this might be a good thing to get.

Power and Modulation Meters

These are meters that allow you to check how well your transmitter is working. A power meter reads the amount of power that your transmitter is putting out in watts (usually about 3 watts). These meters are only accurate when used with an antenna that has a very low SWR. As with an SWR meter, this meter is connected between the output of the transceiver and the antenna. A short piece of coaxial cable, with a coax plug on both ends , is used to link the meter and the transceiver. Since you are measuring the power of the carrier, a power meter will be equally accurate with AM or FM.

A modulation meter measures approximately the modulation of AM CBs only. Although there are deviation meters that can measure FM deviation, these are expensive and not readily available as a consumer item. There are even combination meters that measure SWR, power and modulation within the same package.

Some power meters also contain a field strength indicator. This requires the use of a small whip antenna which screws onto the meter. With a field strength meter you can get a relative indication of the radiated strength of a signal coming off the antenna. With the aid of this device antenna comparisons can be made and the directivity of beam antennas checked.

Combination FM and CB Receivers

There are several inexpensive combination receivers that not only allow you to receive the CB band, but also include the VHF FM Broadcast Band, aeronautical mobile band and VHF TV Bands. These units come with a tuning knob and squelch control. It is even possible to pick up other stations on these includ-

Fig. 8-9 Micronta Field Strength/SWR Tester (Courtesy Radio Shack Div. of Tandy)

ing airplanes, police, fire and other public service stations. Featuring low battery consumption, light-weight operation and low-cost, these receive-only units can be an excellent buy.

External Speakers

Having an external speaker on your CB adds an extra dimension to listening. Better fidelity as well as louder reception can result with their use. In some instances, such as driving a big wheeler or other noisy truck, an external speaker pointed at the driver will help out. Since most CBs end up under the dash with their speakers directed at the floor, an external speaker gets the sound up to where you can hear it.

Antenna Switches

An antenna switch usually comes in a small box that can be mounted some place near your radio. You plug the coaxial lead-in from different antennas into the switch and run a short coax jumper to the transceiver. These are very handy when using a beam and a vertical antenna. You can monitor on the vertical and switch over to the beam to make a connection with a particular station.

Antenna Matchers

Antenna matchers are useful when you have an antenna that has a high SWR. They can prevent the high SWR from damaging the final power amplifier of your transmitter. You'll get out much better if you use an antenna that has a low SWR than if you try to match a bad antenna system with one of these. Antenna matchers do not improve SWR at the antenna. They only make it so that the high SWR does not reach the transmitter.

VFO

VFO stands for *Variable Frequency Oscillator*, but on the CB band it is commonly known as a slider. A VFO can enable a CB operator to be able to slide his CB radio up above, below or even in-between the authorized CB channels. This device is only legal as a receive-only adapter. If it is used to transmit as well as receive, it is illegal.

Phone Patches

A phone patch can prove to be fairly handy. It allows you to connect a CB radio up to your telephone. For example, if you were driving your car and needed to get a message across town to someone on the telephone, you can call back to your base and have someone there turn on the phone patch and dial the number you want to call. You could then speak directly over the telephone via CB. This requires someone at the base station to press the mike button when the party on the phone talks. In some countries, the hook-up of a two-way radio to the public telephone system is illegal. Check with your local regulations before using one of these.

Frequency Counters

These actually read the transmitted frequency of your CB, flashing a digital readout that gives the frequency to five or more digits. When transmitting on channel 1, for example, a signal dead on frequency would read 26.965 MHz (27.60125 MHz on FM rigs in the UK and Ireland). Frequency counters are becoming increasingly popular as base station accessories.

Fig. 8-10 OPTO-Electronics 0-1300 MHz frequency counter (Courtesy OPTO-Electronics)

Receiver Preamps or Booster

These usually come in a box that plugs in betweeen your antenna and your transceiver. They amplify all the signals coming into your receiver. These are especially good for those transceivers that lack volume or sensitivity on receive. Receiver amplifiers can be used on many kinds of base station radios to extend the amplification of the receiver. They operate off of 120 or 240 volts AC. Some of them have a tuneable gain control, a nice feature for a base station if you don't already have it.

Bilateral Amplifiers

This is a combination of a receiver preamp and a linear amplifier. In other words, it works both ways. It helps on both receive and transmit.

Radar Detectors

This is a piece of electronic gadgetry which detects police radar. It is sold as an accessory for mobile use. This gives you forewarning that your speed is being clocked. Some flash a light; others ring buzzers or both.

Fig. 8-11 Uniden RD 25 Radar Detector (Courtesy Uniden)

PA Horn

These can be attached to any CB having a PA system. They come in either metal or plastic, (metal is more durable) and may be mounted outdoors or under the hood.

Power Reducers or Attenuators

These are devices that hook into your coax line to reduce the effective radiated power (ERP) of your station. Some of these have a relay switch which connects the device on transmit only, so that the station's receive capabilities are not cut back along with the transmitted signal.

TV Interference Filters (How to Stay at Peace with the Neighbors)

Folks who are into radio encounter one thorny problem fairly frequently. Their CB radio transmissions can interfere with TV reception in the neighborhood, causing distortion to the picture and sound reception of nearby TV sets. Most CBs will not bother a properly built TV unless they are fairly close to each another. However, some TVs have a receiver that is not selective enough to reject a strong nearby CB signal. And occasionally a radio out of adjustment will radiate interference that will mess up TV reception at locations nearby. Whenever possible, the offending CB antenna should be mounted as far as possible from your neighbor's TV aerial. This will sometimes clear it up. If that doesn't do it, you can get a low-pass filter that plugs in between your CB and your antenna. Low pass filters are carried by most radio supply houses. Before using a low pass filter, be sure that your CB antenna has an SWR below 1.5 to 1.

Some low pass filters are adjustable so that you can tune them while watching a color TV signal. If you can tune out TV interference to your own TV set, this often is sufficient proof to your neighbors that it is their TV and not your radio at fault. This can be easily demonstrated to them in your own home. If you use a tuneable low pass filter, use an SWR meter to monitor the SWR while adjusting the filter. Adjust for maximum elimination of TV interference while maintaining minimum SWR. If the interference persists, try putting a high-pass filter on the TV set. To do this, disconnect the wires connecting the TV antenna to the back of the TV set and connect them to the terminals on the high-pass filter. Then connect the leads from the high-pass filter to the TV set.

Dummy Loads

A dummy load is a device that can take the place of an antenna for testing purposes. It plugs into the antenna jack on your rig and you can transmit without going out over the air. A dummy load is nothing more than a 50-ohm resistor. Small 5-watt light bulbs are sometimes used as dummy loads.

Tone Squelch

Tone squelch is available as optional equipment for some transceivers. It cuts off your receiver's volume and puts it on stand-by until another radio equipped with tone squelch of the same type triggers your receiver to come on. The advantage of that is that you don't have to sit and listen to other stations on a channel in order to monitor for someone else with the same tone squelch. It's a private signaling device.

Phaser Lasers, Gooney Birds, Roger Bleeps, and Pings

There are several kinds of signaling devices that can be installed inside your mike or radio. They are used to attract attention. A phaser laser sounds like a sound effect from *Star Wars* and a gooney bird is like an electronic bird call. These effects are controlled by a switch so that you can turn them on anytime during a transmission. Roger Bleeps were originally used by the US astronauts. They emit a short bleep when the mike is un-keyed automatically, to let the other station know every time a transmission is finished. A ping is a tone that comes on when the mike is keyed and trails off in a second. All of these devices have been banned for use on CB by various national telecommunications authorities including the U.S. Federal Communications Commission.

Chapter Nine

Emergency Procedures

There are many times when CB is the quickest or the only way to get help in an emergency situation. **You might be the one** to come across a motorist off in a ditch or in need of assistance.

First, determine what kind of assistance you need and how you can best get this assistance. If you are on the interstate or freeway, there will be a lot of mobile stations on the trucker channel. Also, if mechanical assistance such as a wrecker is needed, you may find a local wrecking service monitoring the trucker channel. There may be a Smokey on this channel, too, if you need one.

It might be best to get in touch with a base station that has a telephone land line if you can't get direct assistance.

Channel 9 is the National Emergency and Highway Assistance channel. There are base and mobile stations all over the country that monitor Channel 9 for this purpose. Here is an example of how to get help on Channel 9:

THIS IS   (call sign)   AT   (exact location)   IN NEED OF ASSISTANCE. IS THERE A BASE STATION ON THE CHANNEL? OVER.

It's likely that a station will respond to your call with his call sign and ask what he or she can do to help.

If the situation is a life and death emergency, you can get on the air and break for a 10-33.

144

BREAK. BREAK. BREAK.* WE HAVE A 10-33 AT   (exact location). THIS IS   (call sign)   REQUESTING   (police, medical, etc.)   ASSISTANCE.   OVER.

If you can't make contact on Channel 9, try other channels. After making contact on another channel, you can change to Channel 9 to pass any needed information.

You should stay at the scene until you are no longer needed.

If you hear an emergency situation, you should immediately stop all transmitting and listen to see if the station involved is getting assistance. If another station is already helping out, it is probably best to just listen for awhile to see if it's covered.

In some situations you might have to answer the call for help. In this case, keep all transmissions as short as possible and speak clearly, giving the station your call sign and location.

Write down all information, including:

- Station's call sign or handle
- Exact location of emergency
- Description of emergency
- Type of help needed
- Time

Ask the station to remain at the scene in case there is any furthur need for communication.

After making any necessary calls, let the station know help is on the way. Stay in contact if possible until help arrives.

It's a good idea to announce the situation on the trucker channel if it is a highway accident.

You shouldn't transmit on any of the 40 channels while you are within a mile of the emergency scene if other stations are passing emergency traffic. You might bleed over onto Channel 9 or any other channel if you are close.

It's a good idea not to use channel 8 or 10 on the highway at all, because you might tend to bleed over onto Channel 9. This goes for skip talkers too. The main thing is to listen closely and pay good attention.

---

* The international distress signal, **MAYDAY** may be used instead of **BREAK, BREAK, BREAK** by some maritime or other stations.

Chapter Ten

Fixing Your Rig or What Went Wrong

If something goes wrong with your rig, there are quite a few things that you can do to make it work again or to find out what's wrong with it.

One thing you have to keep in mind when working with CBs or any kind of electrical equipment is *Safety First*. All CB radios that directly run off of house AC mains have high voltage in them. Definitely enough to kill you. So take it easy and pay good attention.

You can't hurt yourself with the voltages in a 12-volt mobile transistor rig but you can burn out the rig if you're not careful.

There are certain safety precautions that you need to know if you're going to take the cover off your radio:

• Never take the cover off the radio with the power cord plugged in. This includes 12-volt transistorized rigs.

• Move any metal objects or wires out from around or under the radio when testing or working on it.

• Never turn on the rig without the correct fuse in the fuse holder.

- Don't operate your rig during a lightning storm. Don't touch any components inside the radio while the power is connected.

- Don't touch or turn on the radio if it or you are wet.

Fig. 10-1 Troubleshooting set-up

Most of the time the different problems that come up with CB rigs are external to the rig itself-such as the antenna, microphone, connectors and wires.

If you are going to get inside your rig be sure you know what you're doing. Just twiddling around in a rig can decrease its overall efficiency.

On some occasions when your rig goes out, it will be necessary to take it to a radio repairman who has the test equipment and knowledge to do the job. But many times the problem is simple and you can figure it out on your own. The US FCC says that only technicians with a general radiotelephone license can legally repair any frequency-determining or power output circuits. This is to prevent you from accidentally tuning your radio up off frequency or above the legal power limit.

Troubleshooting Guide

RECEIVING	
Symptoms	*What to do*
1. No dial lights, no receive, set is dead.	1. Is it plugged in? Check to see if power switch is on. Check to see if fuse is blown. If it is, replace it with another fuse of the same rating. Don't use aluminum foil. Check for possible frayed wires or skinned-off insulation. If it is a mobile, sometimes the ignition key must be turned on for the rig to get it's juice. Check connections where the rig gets its power. Check ground connections.
2. Can receive but cuts in and out. Dial lights blink.	2. Intermittent connection to power or battery. Check fuse holder. Check ground connection. Make sure that screws are tight on all mounts. Wiggle power cord and antenna coaxial cable-see if it makes the power cut on and off. Check power plug on transceiver.

Receiving *(cont.)*	
Symptoms	*What to do*
3. Dial lights come on, but no receive.	3. Check squelch knob and make sure the mike cord is plugged in. Make sure PA switch is in CB position. Wiggle microphone cord and connector. If it cuts in and out, there might be a loose connection in the connector or mike. In this case the mike cord might need to be cut-off and re-soldered.
4. Receiving only very near-by stations.	4. Is the antenna connected? How is the SWR? If the SWR is high, possibly there is a short in the coax or connectors. Check local/distant switch—should be in the distant position. Check RF gain knob, it should be all the way up. If the rig is a tube type base station unit, check all the tubes.
5. Receiving only hiss.	5. Check the antenna and connector. Take antenna connector off and put it back on again. If that makes any difference in the hiss, try other channels and a radio check with a nearby station.

Receiving *(cont.)*	
Symptoms	*What to do*
6. Fuse blows when rig is turned on.	6. Short or blown transistor inside radio. Check to see if screws or mounting bolts are touching any components or wires inside the radio. Do not replace the fuse with a larger fuse or aluminum foil. This can cause further damage to your radio.
7. Stations received move S-meter, but do not come on through speaker clearly or not at all.	7. Check the squelch knob. If the speaker sounds fuzzy, try plugging an external speaker in. If this works, you might have to replace the speaker. Check wires leading to the speaker inside the radio. Could also be a bad audio transistor.
8. Nearby stations sound fuzzy.	8. If they're within 100 feet, this might be normal. Try switching local/distant switch to local, or turning the RF gain down.

Receiving (cont.)	
Symptoms	*What to do*
9. Smoke comes out of top of rig when turned on.	9. By all means turn it off! Pull the plug. Check to see what size fuse is in the fuse holder. It should be no more than 3 amps for a transistorized radio. Check the polarity of the battery connections in a mobile. Check to see that the negative and positive wires are hooked up right. If you are using an external speaker, make sure that none of the wires leading to it touch the chassis of the radio or the body of your vehicle. After disconnecting the radio from the power, replace the fuse with one of the proper value. Check to see if any screws or mounting bolts touch components inside the radio. If the polarity was reversed, try out the rig again. If the fuse blows again, there is probably a blown diode or transistor.
10. Receiver just hums.	10. Microphone may not be plugged in. If the radio uses an external power supply, it might be blown. Try the radio on a car battery or another DC power supply. If it's a tube-type base station unit, there might be a tube or capacitor out.

TRANSMITTING	
Symptoms	*What to do*
1. When mike button is pushed, receiver does not cut out—cannot transmit.	1. Check the microphone cord and microphone switch. You might have pulled some of the wires loose in the connector. These can just be resoldered to the proper pins inside the connector. If the radio has a relay, it might need to be replaced or cleaned.
2. Transmits a carrier, but no modulation.	2. If you can receive OK, the problem is probably in the microphone cord. Check PA/CB switch.
3. No carrier, no modulation.	3. Could be a bad crystal. Check mike cord. Try different channels.
4. One or more channels not working.	4. Crystal or crystal oscillator is not working. Could be channel selector switch. Spray channel switch contacts with TV-type tuner cleaner.
5. Fuse blows when transmitting.	5. Blown power transistor. Screw or bolts possibly shorting against components inside the radio. Possible short in the antenna connector or antenna.

Transmitting *(cont.)*	
Symptoms	*What to do*
6. Only getting out ¼ mile or so. Relative power meter reads zero.	6. Check antenna and coax cable SWR. For tube-type base station units, the antenna load and plate adjustment screws might need to be set by a qualified technician. If all these are OK, the final RF power transistor might be blown. Have it replaced by a qualified technician.
7. Transmitter "breaking up". Choppy transmissions.	7. Probably a loose connection somewhere. If it only does it on transmit, it's probably the microphone or cord. If on transmit and receive, it might be the antenna or coax cable. Check the ground on the antenna to make sure it is making a solid connection to the vehicle's body.
8. Squealing on transmit.	8. Loose wire in the microphone or cord. If you are using a power mike, try turning it down slightly. If this doesn't help, try a new battery in it. Make sure that the aluminum foil shielding in the power mike isn't shorting anything out after you change the battery.

Transmitting *(cont.)*

Symptoms	What to do
9. Your voice heard from speaker when transmitting. Howling.	9. Check the PA/CB switch. Also check the external speaker wires and PA speaker wires to see if they're grounding out to the body of the vehicle or radio. Also check for a short in the microphone or connector.
10. Weak modulation.	10. If you're using a crystal microphone, the mike element might need to be replaced. A tube or transistor could also be blown.
11. Modulation distorted.	11. Power mike up too high, the antenna is out of whack, the mike gain up too high, or the microphone might need to be replaced.

Note: Sometimes a loose tube or crystal can prevent your rig from working properly. So check all plug-in parts to make sure that they fit snugly in place. Some radios, especially older models, have open relays. Dirty contacts can prevent a radio from switching from transmit to receive. Clean the contacts using a burnishing tool or by pulling a dollar bill through them while holding them lightly together.

Repairing Microphone & Antenna Connections

Tips on Soldering

All electrical soldering is done with rosin-core (not acid-core) solder. Acid-core tends to corrode electrical connections. You can test to see if the soldering iron is hot enough by touching the solder to the tip. It should melt easily. It's a good idea to practice on a couple of wires before trying to solder your microphone cable.

When soldering wires, it's a good idea to "tin" the wires before soldering. You tin the wires by heating the end of the wire up with the iron and applying a small amount of solder to the iron and the wire—just enough to put a thin coat on the wire. Make sure not to melt the plastic insulation while doing this.

Attach or stick the wire in the terminal you want to solder it to. The connector and wire should be held steadily while soldering. When you solder, put the tip of your iron so that it rests on the wire and the terminal at the same time, and apply enough solder for it to flow over the wire and terminal evenly. Never apply any more solder than is necessary to hold it well. Don't move the connection until you're sure the solder has set. It should be nice and shiny.

Fig. 10-2 Soldering tools

Antenna Connections

The antenna is another place where a lot of connections go bad due to weathering and movement. The most common antenna problems are in the coaxial lines and connectors. An insulator at the base of an antenna can break or wear out and cause a short. Sometimes a temporary repair can be made with electrical tape.

Also, if the coax is run through an open window or door, the line can get crimped or cut. In this case, if there is enough excess coax, you can cut off the cable at the break and reconnect it to the antenna. Cutting the coax on magnet mounts is not recommended because the coax acts as the ground part of that type of antenna. If a crimp appears in the coax for a magnet mount, the entire piece of coax should be replaced by one of an equal length.

Coax Splices

It's best to have your coax be one long unbroken run from your rig to the antenna. If splices have to be made in the line, you'll want to make sure there is good electrical contact made. Use two male PL 259 coax connectors and a double female connector. Generously cover this complete assembly and any other external coax connections with a waterproof coax sealing compound to protect them from moisture.

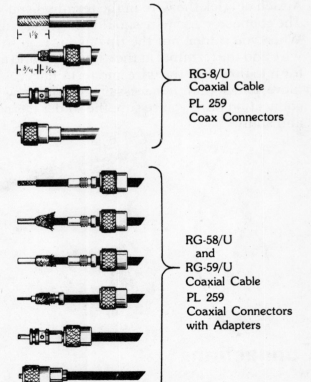

Fig. 10-3 Coax connectors

RG-8/U
Coaxial Cable
PL 259
Coax Connectors

RG-58/U
and
RG-59/U
Coaxial Cable
PL 259
Coaxial Connectors
with Adapters

Soldering Coax Connectors

You'll need some basic tools, a soldering iron, rosin core solder (60.40), medium wirecutters and a knife.

Step One: The most common coaxial connector on most rigs is called a PL-259. It comes apart into three separate pieces.

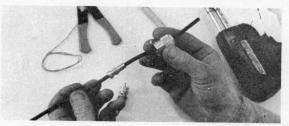

Step Two: Slip adapter and outer cylinder over the cable.

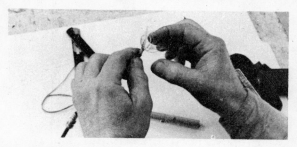

Step Three: Slip outer insulation back 1¼ inches. Make sure not to nick or break the copper braid underneath. Separate the strands of braided shield very carefully; don't cut or break any of them off.

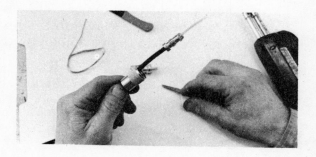

Step Four: Slide the adapter up to the end of the black outer insulation and bend the shield down over it. Then cut the shield so that it doesn't extend down over the threads of the adapter.

(The larger RG-8 coax doesn't require an adapter. Here the braided shield is folded back over the insulation.)

Step Five: Slip the insulation off the center conductor of the coax, leaving a little more than ¼ inch of insulation next to the adapter. If you nick the center wire, start over again, because a nicked wire here will eventually break if much stress is put on it.

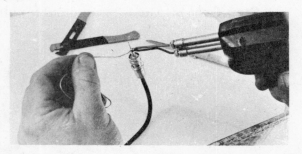

Step Six: Slip the remaining part over the inner conductor and adapter, making sure none of the braid strands slip up and touch the center conductor. (With RG 8, the remaining part of the connector slips on over the braid tightly, holding it in place without the aid of an adapter.)

Step Seven: Solder the inner conductor to the tip of the connector. Let the solder flow into the tip a little bit, but not too much or you'll drip it way down into the connector, shorting it out.

Step Eight: Cut the inner conductor off flush with the tip and screw the outer cylinder back over the rest of the connector.

Microphone Connections

The microphone cord, with all its pulling and moving around, is often a source of trouble. Sometimes a wire comes loose inside the connector where it plugs into the rig. Sometimes, due to flexing, a wire will even break inside the cord where you can't see it, especially at the points where it goes into the connector or the microphone. You can usually tell when this is the case by transmitting, holding the microphone steady while talking, and wiggling the mike cord in various places.

To check the microphone connector, take it apart on a flat clean surface. For some connectors you will need a small jeweler's or Phillips head screwdriver. Take out all the screws in the connector and put them in a safe place. Then take apart the two halves of the connector, or the cover, depending on the type of connector. If one of the wires is broken just solder it back onto the pin. Make sure that it does not touch any of the other pins or bare wires.

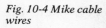
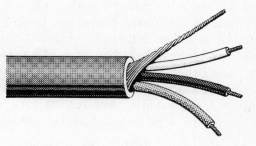

Fig. 10-4 Mike cable wires

Sometimes it may be necessary to cut the cord off and resolder the whole thing. Cut it off about 4 cm (2″) back from the connector. Then cut the outer jacket back 1 or 2 cm (1″) from the end of the cable, being very careful not to nick the insulation on any of the wires inside the cable. Unwind the outer braided shield from around the inner wires and twist the small wires of the shield tightly together. Strip about ⅛ inch of insulation off the tips of the inner wires and tin these tips as well as the twisted tip of the shield.

Now you're ready to solder the wire to the connector. Be sure you have slipped the outer covering or case of the connector over the cable before soldering (depends on the type of connector). Now take one of the old wires off one of the pins of the connector and resolder the new wires of the same color to that pin. Do all the rest of the wires the same way. Be sure you have the right colors on the right pins. The pins are usually numbered right on the connector. Make sure no stray strands of wire touch any other pins or the metal case.

Now you're ready to reassemble the connector case. Make sure the cable clamp firmly grips the outer jacket of the mike cord, taking all the strain off the connections.

For some of the more complicated microphones, such as power mikes, this could be more difficult because you can't get at the connections as well. You might want to have this done by a technician.

Using a Continuity Tester

Whether you are checking out old connections or double checking new ones that you've just made, a continuity tester can be quite handy. This inexpensive tool has a battery which connects to a light bulb, like a flashlight. Instead of having a switch to light the bulb, the continuity tester has a thin metal probe on one end and a long wire ending with an alligator clip on the other end. When the clip and probe are touched together, the battery connection to the bulb is completed and the light goes on. The probe can be touched to one end of any wire and the clip connected to the other end. If the suspect wire is broken, the connection will be uncompleted and the bulb will not light. If the wire is unbroken (or continuous) electricity reaches the light letting you know that a proper connection exists.

This kind of tool is very useful, because you can get a visual indication of whether any particular connection is broken or shorted to ground. A mike cord can be checked for broken wires by connecting the probe end to one of the mike connector pins and the slip end to where the cable connects to the switch inside the mike. Coaxial jumpers can be checked for opens or shorts with this device. Touch the probe to one coax connector outer shield and the clip to the other connector's shield. The light should come on. You can repeat the process by connecting to the tip ends of each connector. A short will show up if you attach the probe to the tip and the clip to the outer shell. If the bulb lights in this situation you probably have a short. You should note however that many types of base-loaded mobile and base-station antennas use a shunt-type coil between the hot and ground of the antenna. This would look like a short to a continuity tester if it was hooked across the antenna's connector. If you want to check the coax, you must first disconnect the antenna from the coaxial line. Most antenna problems are either at the connector itself or at the base of the antenna where the coax hooks in.

Replacing Crystals

Most inexpensive walkie-talkies are limited to operating from just a few of the available CB channels. Crystals for these rigs plug into little sockets. It's as easy as plugging in a lamp. When you buy your walkie talkie, the salesman will make sure that you have the right crystals for the particular model you buy. However, you may wish to add or change channels at some future date. Crystals come in several sizes and styles for different radios, so be sure to check the frequency. You can have crystal frequencies looked up for you in a parts replacement book in a parts store. Even if the crystals have the right channel number printed on them, they still may be the wrong type for your particular rig. So check the frequency of your transmit and receive crystals and buy similar crystals for replacement.

Most rigs that only have a few channels use two crystals for each channel. One crystal is used for transmitting and the other for receiving. The most common types use a receive crystal frequency that is 455 kilohertz less than the transmit crystal frequency. The way to find out if your rig uses this type of crystal is to subtract the frequency of the receive crystal from the frequency of the transmit crystal of the same channel. The frequencies are usually stamped in the metal case of the crystal. This kind of crystal is usually in the 26 to 28 MHz (Megahertz) frequency range.

The chart on the next page gives the most commonly available crystal receive and transmit frequencies for normal CB operations. One word of caution is in order, however. When putting in any new crystals, be sure that the transmit crystal goes in the transmit socket and the receive crystal in the receive socket. If the crystals were inadvertantly placed in the wrong sockets, your walkie talkie would actually transmit on lower frequencies that lie just below the regular CB band. That would leave you with only the occasional skip talker to ratchet jaw with and he's not likely to hear you very well on your puny little handheld rig. Out of band operations are also illegal.

Most new 40-channel rigs use a *Phase Lock Loop*. This is a circuit that uses only one or two crystals and quite a few inexpensive integrated circuits to take the place of many crystals to produce the channels. This is a money saving circuit, since the cost of

Crystal Frequencies

Channel	Transmit	Receive	Channel	Transmit	Receive
1	26.965	26.510	21	27.215	26.760
2	26.975	26.520	22	27.225	26.770
3	26.985	26.530	23	27.255	26.800
4	27.005	26.550	24	27.235	26.780
5	27.015	26.560	25	27.245	26.790
6	27.025	26.570	26	27.265	26.810
7	27.035	26.580	27	27.275	26.820
8	27.055	26.600	28	27.285	26.830
9	27.065	26.610	29	27.295	26.840
10	27.075	26.620	30	27.305	26.850
11	27.085	26.630	31	27.315	26.860
12	27.105	26.650	32	27.325	26.870
13	27.115	26.660	33	27.335	26.880
14	27.125	26.670	34	27.345	26.890
15	27.135	26.680	35	27.355	26.900
16	27.155	26.700	36	27.365	26.910
17	27.165	26.710	37	27.375	26.920
18	27.175	26.720	38	27.385	26.930
19	27.185	26.730	39	27.395	26.940
20	27.205	26.750	40	27.405	26.950

crystals is many times that of integrated circuits. The integrated circuits, which are a product of the computer revolution, divide and multiply together the vibrations of the one or two crystals to produce many channels. *IC chips* are blobs of plastic with little wires sticking out the sides. They look like spiders. The IC chips used in Phase Lock Loops contain transistor logic circuits that are programmed to produce the proper order of the channels.

A few of the older 40-channel rigs are synthesized. This means that they use only a few crystals to make all the channels. The crystal frequencies are added and subtracted together in order to use fewer crystals. Usually if a single crystal goes bad in a synthesized unit, it will make 4 or 5 channels not work. Sometimes the manual that comes with the radio will list the channel numbers on the crystals for the channels they are used on. These can be reordered from the manufacturer. They should be installed by a licensed repairman.

How to Get Rid of Noise

The object of noise suppression is to capture those loose noises made by your vehicle's electrical system and run them to ground before they have a chance to reach your receiver. These noises are usually created by sparks originating from your spark plugs, distributor, accessory motors, alternator, regulator, or gauges. The sparks are electrical impluses that put out static much like little transmitters. There are various ways to keep these sparks from radiating energy that your receiver will pick up. Most of this kind of noise is picked up by the antenna. Most of the time in a car or a truck with a gas-powered engine, the ignition system (spark plugs, distributor, ignition wire and coil) causes most of the noise. Diesel-powered engines have no spark plugs, so there is no ignition noise.

Ignition noise is recognized by a loud popping or crackling, increasing to a buzz when you rev up the motor. If you rev up your engine to a high speed and then shut the key off, the moment you shut it off the ignition noise should stop.

One of the *best remedies* for this kind of noise is to install *radio resistance spark plug wires*. These are available in almost all auto parts stores. Also, radio resistance type spark plugs will cut down ignition noise quite a lot. After installing these the engine should be retimed and tuned at a reputable garage. If you're already using them and still get a lot of noise you might need to suppress other sources of noise.

Another source of noise is the alternator. There are various kinds of suppressors available for alternators that you can get at places where CBs are sold. Alternator noise sounds like a whine that varies with the engine's speed. Usually, an alternator noise suppressor in the battery lead of the alternator clears up the whine.

Noise is sometimes caused by heater and wiper motors and gauges. This kind of noise can be easily remedied by the addition of a coaxial capacitor. This is the kind that's found in most radio stores. It has two screw terminals. Sometimes it might be necessary to drill a hole somewhere close to the motor or the gauge to mount it.

To hook it up you cut the hot wire leading to the motor and strip off the insulation ¼ inch back. Then connect the two ends you now have to the two screw terminals on the capacitor.

Noise from the ignition system occasionally comes through the wires leading to the radio. The noise is picked up in the engine compartment or on the battery leads and channeled to the radio by the wires. In this case, an RF choke and capacitor should be used on the hot lead going to the CB. Also coaxial cable can be run up to the battery, grounding the shield and using the inner conductor to run the juice to the rig. Make sure to use an in-line fuse where it attaches to the battery connection.

Another kind of static is caused by bare wires or loose connections shorting or arcing to the frame or other wires in the vehicle. This is usually noticed on bumpy roads. One way to find which wires are doing this is to listen on the radio with the engine stopped, ignition switch on. Wiggle wires under the dashboard and in the engine compartment. If any static is found, tape up or repair the wires.

The regulator is another frequent cause of static. It's usually noticed as a clicking or intermittant popping sound. When the engine is just starting up or when the headlights are turned on, it tends to come on stronger. To clear this up, make sure that the regulator case and mounting screws have a good electrical connection to the body. You may also need to add .1 MFD coaxial feed-through capacitors on the battery wire leading to the regulator. Caution: don't use this type of capacitor on the field connection of the regulator. There's a special kind of suppressor for use on the field connection.

Generally, gasoline-powered vehicles will be a lot noisier than diesel-powered because there are no spark plugs in a diesel engine. Spark plug or ignition noise is the main cause of static in an automobile. Even if you try all the suppression methods possible you may not be able to cut down all of the spark plug noise without making your engine not work. But you should be able to cut it down quite a lot—enough to make listening enjoyable.

For the real rough cases there are marine-type shielded ignition harnesses available. These will cut out almost all ignition noise from the spark plugs. They're fairly expensive, but they're very dependable. You would probably have to order them through a two-way communications outlet or a marine engine distributor.

Here's another thing that we've tried for cutting down static from the distributor. Get a large-size can, big enough to just fit over the distributor. You can mount it down with a couple of angle brackets to the engine block. The can should be connected securely to the engine block to make a good ground. Make sure that your ignition wires are in good condition if you do this, because if there are any cracks in the insulation they will probably arc across to the can. You need to cut the bottom and top out of the can or make suitable holes for the ignition wires to come out of the top. Make sure you get the ignition wires back on the distributor in the proper order. There should be no sharp edges left on the can that could wear through the ignition wires. We've experienced a drop in ignition noise by half on some vehicles using this method.

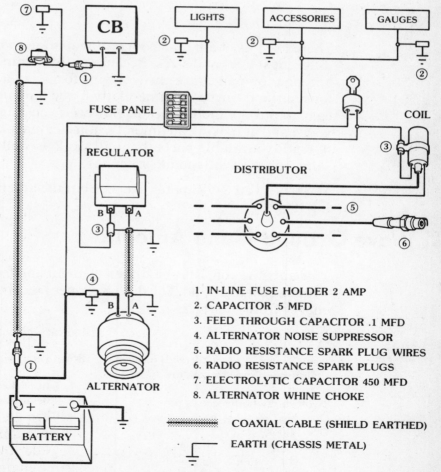

Fig. 10-5 Noise suppression diagram

1. IN-LINE FUSE HOLDER 2 AMP
2. CAPACITOR .5 MFD
3. FEED THROUGH CAPACITOR .1 MFD
4. ALTERNATOR NOISE SUPPRESSOR
5. RADIO RESISTANCE SPARK PLUG WIRES
6. RADIO RESISTANCE SPARK PLUGS
7. ELECTROLYTIC CAPACITOR 450 MFD
8. ALTERNATOR WHINE CHOKE

COAXIAL CABLE (SHIELD EARTHED)

EARTH (CHASSIS METAL)

Chapter Eleven

Do-It-Yourself Antennas

There are lots of antennas out on the market today, all kinds of different shapes and sizes. Because of this competitive market, antenna companies are always trying to put out a better product for a cheaper price. Commercially-made antennas are usually easy to put up and maintain. However, you might want to try your hand at making an antenna. You can make an antenna out of readily-available parts that will work as well or better than some commercially-made antennas.

You'll need an SWR meter to check out the antenna after building it.

¼ Wave Ground Plane Antenna

This antenna consists of a driven element and four radial wires which act as a ground. The driven element receives the transmit energy from the rig.

Parts List   **Note:** British measurements will be in italic.

104" (264 cm.) [*102" (259 cm.)*] piece of aluminum pipe or conduit, ¾" or 1" diam.

Two U-bolts, same size as pipe

One sheet metal screw

One J-hook

Four "egg" ceramic insulators

408" (10.22 m.) [*400" (10.2 m.)*] of 16 gauge wire

Rope, enough to guy the ground radial, depending on the height of the antenna

A couple of two-by-fours

Electrical tape

Silicone sealer to cover coax connection

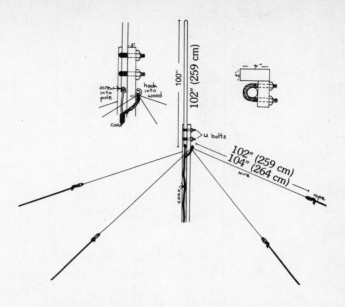

Fig. 11-1–¼ wave ground plane antenna
For American CB use 102" driven element and 104" radial wire.
For British CB use 100" driven element and 102" radial wire.

The inside conductor of the coax is connected to the aluminum pipe by means of a screw into the bottom of the pipe. See the detail drawing on this page. Coat this connection with sealer or cover it with tape to protect it from corrosion.

All vertical antennas need to be grounded in some way. A mobile antenna uses the car body as the ground. On this antenna, the four radial wires are used as the ground. This is called the ground plane of the antenna.

The braided wire which forms the outside conductor of the coax is soldered to all four radial wires. The wires must be exactly 264 cm (104") long [*259 cm(102") long*] (¼ wavelength).

Remember that the inner conductor and outer braid of the coax must not touch each other, nor can the radials come in contact with the driven element. The radials slope down at about a 45° angle in different directions, and are tied to the insulators. Rope of nylon cord is then tied to the insulators and used to hold the radials out. They can be attached to anywhere convenient— trees, a fence, house, etc.

Fig. 11-2 – ¼ wave wire antenna diagram

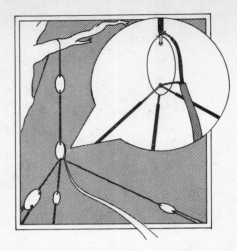

If you are short on room for such a radial system, you can use 264 cm (104″) [*259 cm (102″)*] pieces of aluminum tubing, or suspend the wires on PVC pipe, bamboo, or 1″ x 2″ wooden sticks.

It's a good idea to check the SWR when done. It should be lower than 2, and ideally lower than 1.5 or 1.3.

A ¼ wave ground plane made from wire can be suspended from a tree. We've talked to stations over 40 miles away using this antenna up about 30 feet high, running a mobile rig for a base.

Coax Cable Vertical Antenna

For a quickie antenna, a vertical dipole (½) wave can be made right from the coax itself. You take your coax and very carefully, without nicking the braided shield, strip 102 inches of the outer insulation jacket off one end. After removing the outer jacket, start bunching the shield down the coax from the end. Now, where the outer jacket and the shield meet, separate the braided shield enough to get the inner conductor out through the hole in the braid. Pull all of the inner conductor through and stretch it and the braid out. Be careful not to skin any of the insulation off the inner conductor. Now attach an antenna insulator to the end of the inner conductor. Measure the braided shield. Cut it off at about 106″ and attach an antenna insulator to the end. The total length of the inner and outer conductor should be about 17 feet (½ wave). You can haul it up to any height you want with a string or rope attached to the insulator on the center conductor. It's a good idea to coat the end of the coax cable where it separates with some kind of waterproof sealer. This keeps water from seeping into the coax, which could cause a high SWR.

Just attach a coax connector on the end of the coax going to your transceiver and you're on the air. The SWR should be 1.5 or better, if cut to the proper length. It'll get out about as good as a ¼ wave ground plane antenna if you get it up high and in the

Fig. 11-3 Coax cable vertical antenna

clear. Don't hoist this antenna up next to a metal pole, because the metal will interfere with the antenna's operation and make for a high SWR.

Using a Mobile Antenna for a Base Station

A mobile antenna can be used as a base antenna by mounting it on the top of a metal pipe. The metal pipe serves as ground connection for the antenna, taking the place of the body of the vehicle. Remember to run a separate ground wire to a proper grounding rod for lightning protection.

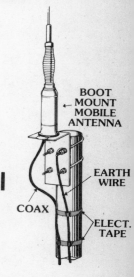

Fig. 11-4 Using a mobile antenna as a base station aerial

Building a Gain Vertical

This is an easy antenna to build and find the parts for. If you follow these instructions and have it come out looking like these pictures, it should have a very low SWR and appreciable gain.

Fig. 11-5 – ⅝ wave ground plane antenna

You can use any number of pieces of aluminum pipe so long as they are ridged and fairly thick-walled so as not to get bent and broken in a strong wind. The pieces should be gradually smaller, one being able to fit inside the next. Cut two 2″ grooves with a hacksaw down the outer pieces of aluminum and put a hose clamp around them. Now adjust the antenna to 22½ feet (6.85 meters) and tighten the hose clamps down to hold it all together. This 22½-foot vertical element can now be mounted with two U-bolts on to the 2″ x 6″ board. This board should be treated or painted to protect it from the weather.

Put a bolt through the piece of wood a few inches below the vertical element. Here you should fasten one end of the 6 foot (183 centemeters) piece of copper wire or tubing, the outside braid of the coax and each of the 104" (264 cm)[*102" (259 cm)*] long, stranded wires. These are called the ground radials and should be tied off with string (not wire) at a 45° angle away from the bolt. The ground radials and the braid from the coax can be soldered together or can be crimped together with a crimp connector which fits the bolt. The other end of the 6' copper wire is bent and fastened to the vertical element as the picture illustrates. The end of the center wire of the coax is then twisted onto this in such a way that it can be slid up or down along the copper wire and soldered after adjustment.

The SWR of this antenna is adjusted by sliding this connection. You do this by keying your rig up on channel 20 and sliding this connection up or down until you have the lowest SWR. In our experience, an SWR of 1.1 or 1 was easily reached on channel 20 with a low SWR throughout the 27 MHz band.

Be sure to cover the end of the coax real well with a moisture-proofing sealing compound so no moisture can get in it.

Fig. 11-6 Close up of a ⅝ wave installation

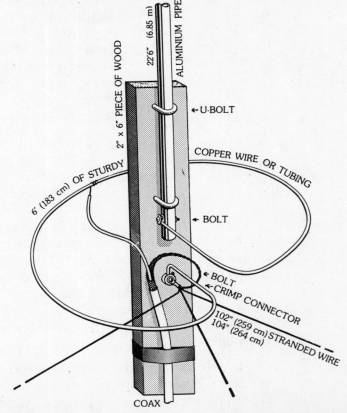

Fishing Pole Ear—A Homemade Mobile Antenna

While the next project won't necessarily save you any money, you might want to give it a try if you are interested in understanding more about how fiberglass whip antennas do their thing. We have talked 30 miles mobile-to-base on one of these homebrew fishing pole antennas using a $20 barefoot rig.

Antenna Parts

One 7-foot fiberglass fishing pole with hollow base
One piece of steel rod 4 to 6 inches long–right diameter to slip into base of pole
One ¼" x 1" machine bolt (threads to match mount)
12 feet of enamel
#18 gauge wire
Some good epoxy glue

Antenna Mount Parts

One ¼" x 2½" bolt and nut (same threads as bolt on base of pole)
One longer-than-usual ¼" nut
Two plastic insulating washers
Three metal ⅝" diameter washers
One large terminal lug

First you've got to get yourself a fishing pole, 6 to 9 feet long. If you already have an old one lying around, you can clip off the line loops and cut the handle off.

We did some shopping and found that a finished fishing pole as long as we wanted was at least as expensive as a newly-manufactured CB antenna. But then we discovered a sporting goods store that sold unfinished fiberglass poles 7-feet long for $6. The kind we found was a black hollow tapered pole with about a ⅝" inside diameter at the base.

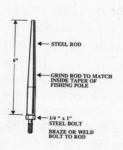

STEEL ROD

6"

GRIND ROD TO MATCH
INSIDE TAPER OF
FISHING POLE

1/4 " x 1"
STEEL BOLT

BRAZE OR WELD
BOLT TO ROD

Fig. 11-7 Tip of a fishing pole ear

The next step is to hook something to the pole so you can screw it to a mount on your vehicle. The way we did it was to get a piece of scrap steel rod near the inside of the base of the hollow pole. (If the pole ain't hollow you'll have to figure out another way of hooking to it.)

Grind a slight taper to match inside taper of the fishing pole. Braze bolt to rod. Use ¼" x 1" steel bolt. Epoxy the steel rod inside the base of the fishing pole.

There are many commercially-made antenna mounts that you can buy at electronic parts stores that could be used to hold your fishing pole ear. If you elect to buy one of these mounts, get one with a spring so that if the pole encounters a stray tree branch, it can bend instead of break! If you are going to use this antenna with a store-bought mount, the threads on the bolt on the bottom of the antenna should mate with the hole in the top of the mount's spring.

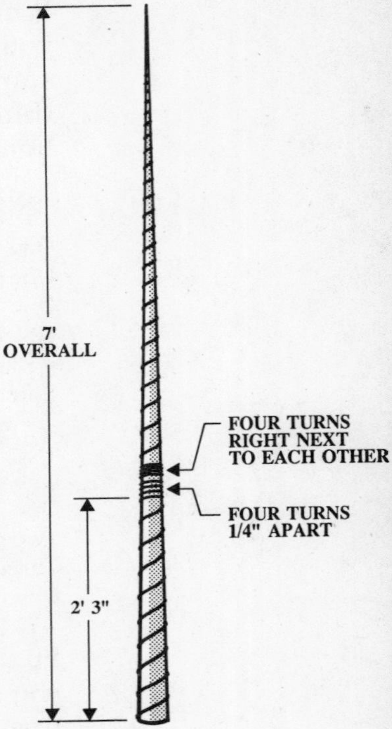

Fig. 11-8 Dimensions of a fishing pole ear

7' OVERALL

FOUR TURNS RIGHT NEXT TO EACH OTHER

FOUR TURNS ¼" APART

2' 3"

Tuning the Fishing Pole Ear

Now it's time to get into the electrical part of the antenna. The fishing pole ain't the antenna; it's just a prop that holds the wire up. So we need to wind a wire around the fishing pole in such a way that will make it tune the 27 MHz CB band.

If your antenna is shorter than 9 feet long, you can tune it by winding a coil around the pole. On our 7-foot ear, we found that it was necessary to make a coil of four turns ¼" apart about 2' 3" up from the base of the pole (see illustration). Tightly wrap the wire in a spiral up from the base of the pole. Make the distance between windings as wide as possible below and above the coil. If you follow these particular dimensions you should be close to being tuned up. To really make the ear a perfect match, however, you'll need to use an SWR meter to check the SWR. You may have to modify the coil spacings or add or subtract a turn from the coil to get it just right.

Different lengths of antennas will also work, but different coil windings will be necessary, so if you have a different length pole you'll have to use a meter to tune it up. You just have to dive right in and try different numbers of coil windings. The longer the pole, the less center coil windings; the shorter, the more windings necessary. It takes some playing around and trial and error.

We used enamel coated wire, the kind used in motor windings, generators, transformers, etc. It's best to use enamel-coated wire so that the coil turns can't possibly short to each other.

At the bottom, wrap the wire around the ¼" bolt. Be sure to scrape the enamel coating off the wire and clean the bolt for good contact. Solder that wire to the bolt or use a nut to hold the wire onto the bolt so that it makes a good electrical connection.

We covered some antennas we made with a thin coat of fiberglass (which you can tint any color you want). They looked pretty good but the fiberglass chipped off some of the antenna tips because they were mounted fairly high up and got tangled in the trees. You can prevent chipping by putting some shrink tubing over the tip. Shrink tubing would be another possible way to hold the wire on the fishing pole. It's available at most electronics shops.

Building a Fishing Pole Antenna Mount

If you are really adventurous, you can also build your antenna mount. The main point to understand when making an antenna mount is that the radiating element is not supposed to ground out to the body of the vehicle. This means that the bolt the antenna hooks to must be insulated from the metal body of the vehicle.

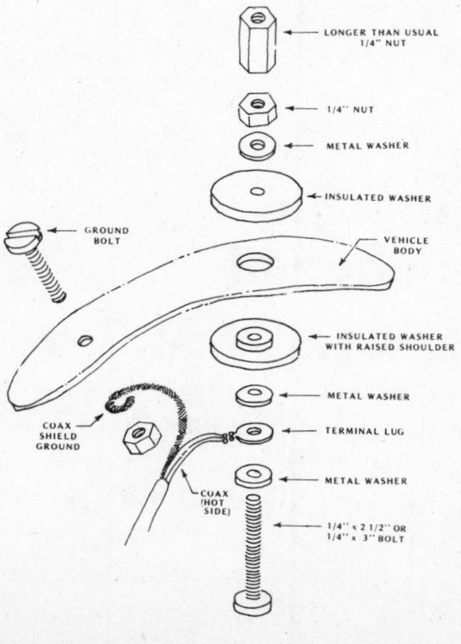

Fig. 11-9 Parts to mount - exploded view

Your homemade mount must use good insulating washers, because if the bolt shorts to the vehicle body it could possibly blow out your rig's final RF power transistor.

One source of homebrew insulating washers is the main output terminals of junk alternators or generators. The washers should be made out of some type of plastic. The best kind of insulating washer has a shoulder around its hole. You drill a hole in the vehicle body, big enough to allow the shoulder to fit through. This holds the bolt away from the metal body.

If you can't find a plastic washer with a shoulder, it is possible to use two flat plastic washers with a little piece of plastic tubing in place of the shoulder. Make sure the plastic is tough enough to not get cut up by the edge of the hole in the vehicle body.

Fig. 11-10
4-element beam

The Long John Antenna
Build a 10 dB gain beam!

A 4-element Long John antenna will make your radio **ten times more powerful** than if you used a ¼-wave vertical antenna. This type of high-gain beam is easy to build. Materials include aluminum plates and tubing, automotive muffler clamps, and radiator hose clamps—all of which are easy enough to find in any large city.

Parts List

4 sections of 1″ (2.5 cm) aluminum tubing, 12 feet (3.7 m) long with .035″ (1 mm) wall

3 sections of 7.8″ (2.2 cm) aluminum tubing, 12 feet (3.7m) long with .035″ (1 mm) wall

1 section of 2 ¼″ (5.6 cm) OD (outside diameter) aluminum pipe 20 feet (6.1 m) long with a thick wall size

1 section ½″ (1.25 cm) aluminum tubing 2 feet (9.6 m) long, any wall thickness

12 2¼″ (5.6 cm) muffler clamps with lock washers

8 1″ (2.5 cm) radiator hose clamps

2 2″ (5 cm) muffler clamps

8 sheet metal screws - No. 8 self tapping

1 plastic box 4″ x 8″ x 2″ (10 x 20 x 5 cm) with sealable lid

4 aluminum plates 4″ x 12″ x ⅛″ (10 x 30 x.3 cm) thick

1 aluminum plate 4″ x 10″ x ⅛″ (10 x 25 x.3 cm) thick

1 aluminum plate 12″ x 12″ x ⅛″ (30 x 30 x .3 cm) thick

1 coax connector–female chassis mount

1 tunable capacitor 0-100 pF-receiver type. (This kind of capacitor can be bought or retrieved out of an old AM radio or other radio junk.)

12 bolts ⅛″ (.3 cm) thick x 1″ (2.5 cm) long with extra lock washers and nuts

1 plastic knob to fit the capacitor's shaft size

8 U bolts 1″ (2.5 cm)

1 piece aluminum sheeting 12″ x 12″ x ¹⁄₃₂″ (30 x 30 x 1 mm) thick

1 small piece of plexiglass 1′ x 3′ x ⅛″ (2.5 x 7.5 .3 cm) thick

1 tube silicone sealer

Tools Needed

Hack saw
wire cutters
adjustable spanner
sheet metal shears
screw driver

metal file
pocket knife
tape measure
electric drill
assorted drill bits

This antenna was designed to have a wide bandwidth so that it could tune from 27.000 to 28.000 MHz with a low SWR. The 6′8″ (2 m) spacing between the elements themselves both contribute to the wide bandwidth. It is possible to build a 5-element beam on the same length of boom using closer spacing (as low as 5 feet or 1.5 m between elements)—but only at the expense of the antenna's bandwidth. Close spacing will also result in less overall gain. In fact, a close-spaced 5 element beam will have no more gain than a wide spaced 4-element one! Close spacing of the elements also makes the antenna tuning adjustment more critical. If the large size of a 4-element beam puts you off, you may want to eliminate the second director element and have a 3-element beam on a shorter boom. But keep the wide spacing between the elements for best overall performance.

Buying The Aluminum

If you can't get the exact wall thickness of tubing that we list, get as close as you can. Make sure that the smaller 7/8" tubing will still fit inside of the larger tubing. If the fit is loose, you may have to make some shims out of sheet metal stock to take up any slack. If you buy your aluminum plates from a sheet metal company, you can often get them to cut the pieces to the exact size you need. We recommend this over having to cut all the pieces out yourself by hand.

It is possible to use a slightly smaller or larger diameter pipe for the supporting boom. But if you switch to another size, you'll also need to change the size of all muffler clamps that attach to the boom.

Assembly of the Beam Antenna

Drilling the aluminum plates. Use a drill bit big enough to allow the muffler clamps to comfortably slide through the holes. The 4" x 12" plate will be used to mount the elements to the boom, and the 12" x 12" plate is for mounting the beam to a supporting pole or mast.

Making the elements. Slice a notch about 4 inches into the ends of each 1" aluminum tube. Make sure that the notch is centered in the middle of the tubing for its full length. File away any aluminum burrs that occur around the notch.

Next, cut the 7/8" tubing into two short pieces for each element. These are the tips of the elements and their length will differ depending on whether they are for the reflector, driven or director elements. Here are their dimensions:

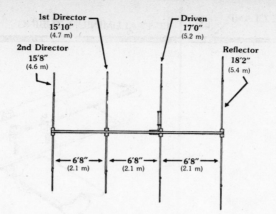

Fig. 11-11 Diagram of a 4-element beam

2 pieces - 4 feet long (1.2 m) - reflector tips
2 pieces - 3½ feet long (1.1 m) - driven elements
2 pieces - 3 feet long (.9 m) - first director tips
2 pieces - 2 feet 10" long (.85 m) - second director tips

Put a mark on each tip piece 1 foot from an end. Slip the reflector tips into each end of a 1" tube so that 1 foot of the tip is inside the larger 1" pipe and the rest extends outside of it. Repeat this procedure when assembling the directors and driven element.

Slip a hose clamp over each junction of 1" to ⅞" pipe. Place the clamp over the 4" slit and tighten until the two sections of pipe are firmly held together. Drill a hole slightly smaller than the size of a No. 8 self-tapping screw about 8 inches back from each end of the 1" pipe. Putting sheet metal screws in helps to anchor the tips to the 1" center sections of the elements.

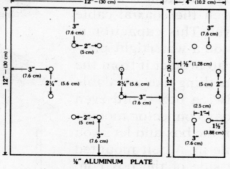

Fig. 11-12 Aluminum mounting plate dimensions

Mounting the elements to the boom. Center each element on one of the 4" x 12" plates. Put the 1" U bolts on and tighten them into place so that the tubing is securely held, but not dented or crimped.

Mark off the 20-foot boom into 6' 8" lengths. Center the plate mounted elements on each of these marks with the reflector first, the driver second, and then the first and second directors. Bolt them in place with the 2" muffler clamps. Make sure that the elements all line up together.

HOSE CLAMP   3"   12'-1" ALUMINIUM TUBING   3"   HOSE CLAMP

*Fig. 11-13 Alumi-
num tubing dimen-
sions*

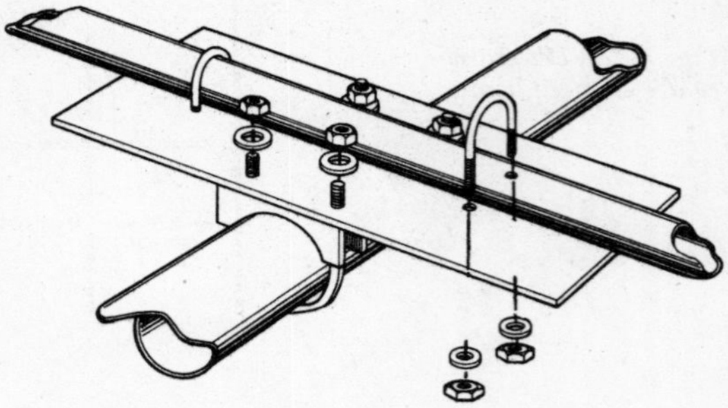

*Fig. 11-14 Tubing
to boom mount*

Feeding the Antenna - The Gamma Match

A beam antenna like the one we are making is fussy about how the radio's power is delivered to it. The antenna must be fed through a balancing device which matches the antenna to the output of the radio and coax. Without the addition of the gamma match, the antenna would have a high SWR and much of the radio's power would be reflected away from the antenna back into the coax. With a gamma match, the antenna can be tuned for a low SWR and the maximum transfer of power from the radio on out to the antenna takes place.

Making the gamma match. The match connects a tunable capacitor in line between the coaxial cable and the driver. This capacitor is mounted inside a watertight plastic container to protect it from the weather. Something like a sealable plastic sandwich box could even work. The coax connector mounts on one end of the box and let's you plug the cable in. A bolt mounted through one side of the box connects to the driven element through a short section of ½" tubing, called the gamma rod. There is a short jumper wire between the bolt and the gamma rod.

*Fig. 11-15
Gamma box*

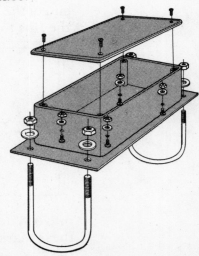

*Fig. 11-16 Gamma
match dimensions*

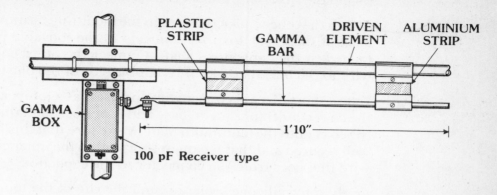

Mount the female coax connector by drilling a good sized hole centered in one end of the plastic box. Carefully widen this hole with your pocket knife until the round part of the connector will fit snugly in place. Mark the four holes that go through the connector and drill them out. Use small bolts to secure this connector to the side of the box.

In the other end of the box drill a hole just big enough to allow the capacitor's tuning shaft to snugly fit through. Mark onto the plastic box where the capacitor's mounting holes should go, and drill them out. Bolt the capacitor in place.

Center the 4″ x 8″ plastic box on top of the 4″ x 10″ aluminum plate. Mark the areas on either end that extends beyond the box. Within that extra space drill holes for mounting a 2 ¼″ muffler clamp on each end of the plate. Take the plastic box and drill an ⅛″ hole in each corner. Center the box again onto the plate and mark the holes onto it. Drill them out and mount the box onto the plate.

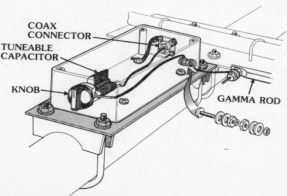

Drill a hole in one side of the box and connect a bolt to it. Add on the nuts and washers in the order pictured.

*Fig. 11-17 Gamma
box connections*

The tunable capacitor consists of two sets of metal plates that can be meshed together by turning the shaft. Solder a wire to the inner conductor of the coax connector.

Attach the other end of the wire to the mounting terminal on the back of the capacitor that connects to the movable plates attached to the capacitor's shaft. Connect the other end of this wire to the bolt that goes through the side of the plastic box.

Take a short piece of copper wire and use it as a jumper between the coax connector's metal base and the closest bolt that fastens the coax onto the aluminum plate. Make sure that this jumper is well secured and that it cannot short out to the inner conductor wire that goes from the connector to the capacitor.

Apply some silicone sealer around the rim of the top and anywhere else where you might think that water could get in. Fasten the lid onto the box. Position the gamma box on top of the boom right next to the driven element, and bolt it in place with a couple of muffler clamps.

The Gamma Rod. Take the section of ½" aluminum tubing and flatten one of the ends. Drill a hole in the flattened end and put a bolt through with a nut and washers.

There are two clamps which fasten the gamma rod to the driven element. The all-metal clamp is made by bending a 2" x 8" strip of aluminum sheeting around the two tubes leaving a spacing of about 3" between them. The second clamp is made out of two short pieces of aluminum with a plexiglass insulator in between the tubes. Unlike the first clamp which is the electrical connection between the rod and the driven element, this second clamp is merely there to give added physical support to the gamma rod.

Run a short jumper wire between the bolt protruding from the gamma box and the bolt on the end of the gamma rod.

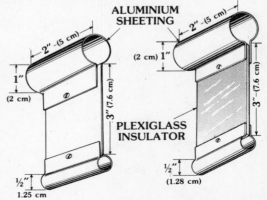

Fig. 11-18 Plexiglass insulator dimensions

Tuning the Gamma Match. In order to do this, you'll need the help of a friend or two. Tilt the antenna back on its reflector and point it straight up in the air. Make sure that no stress is put on the reflector element itself, but on the boom pipe and element plate only. Hook a SWR meter up to the gamma box with a short coaxial jumper. Hook the coax in to the other end. Have someone key up the CB on channel 20 which is in the middle of the CB Band. Don't worry, the two watts or so that your radio puts out will not hurt you. Calibrate the meter in the forward position and put it into the reflected position and take a SWR reading. Adjust the gamma capacitor for the lowest SWR reading. If you can't get the SWR below 1.5 to 1, stop transmitting and adjust the metal clamp that connects the gamma rod to the boom. Move it toward the far end of the gamma rod and take another SWR reading. If the SWR goes down, then readjust the gamma capacitor for the lowest reading. If you still don't have below 1.5 to 1, move the clamp a little further down the rod, until you can get a low SWR. If the SWR went up when you moved the clamp, you may have to reverse directions and move closer to the boom. By adjusting the capacitor and varying the location of the metal clamp connecting between the gamma rod and driven element, you should be able to get a SWR below 1.5. You may have to fine tune your SWR once it is in the air but it should be pretty close to what it was on the ground. Once you have the beam all tuned up and hoisted up there, give someone a shout. We're sure that you'll be getting out!

The Quad
Build This 12 dB Gain Beam!

How about hoisting this one up the flagpole? It definitely looks like she'll fly. It is built out of two or more loops of wire that are supported by fiberglass rods, bamboo or PVC pipe.

Fig. 11-19 Quad antenna

Parts List

110 feet of stranded insulated copper wire, 12-14 gauge, to be cut
   into three separate pieces
One 3″ diameter (thick wall) aluminum pipe, 10-14 ft. long
Twenty-four 3″ hose clamps
20 ft. of 1″ angle aluminum stock
Eight 3″ U-bolts, nuts and lock washers
12″ x 12″ aluminum (or steel) plate, ⅛″ thick
Rubber strips for padding the supports
Fiberglass rods, Bamboo or 1″ PVC pipe
   for drive - 4 pcs., 6 ft. long
   for reflector - 4 pcs., 6 ft. 7in. long
   for director - 4 pcs., 5 ft. 5in. long
One plexiglass plate, approx 6″ x 6″
One roll nylon twine
Two 1½″ U-bolts, nuts and lock washers
One 1½″ o.d. galvanized steel pipe, 6 ft. long

The distance between elements can vary from about 5′ to 6′9″
depending on what size antenna you think you can handle. The
shorter the spacing the less the gain. The advantage of shorter
spacing is in the antenna's compactness and easier maneu-
verability. The distance between the reflector and the driven
element should be a few inches more than between the director
and the driven element. For the highest gain use a spacing of 6′9″
between reflector and driven and 6′3″ between director and
driven elements.

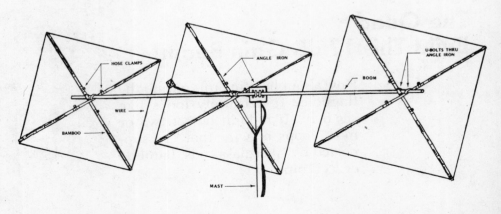

Fig. 11-20 Quad assembly

Assembly of Our Homebrew Quad Antenna

Step 1. Selecting the support members. The material that you pick for the quad's cross arms will determine just how well the antenna will survive after long-term exposure to the elements. While non-conductive fiberglass rods, like those used for the manufacture of fishing poles are the best in terms of tensile strength, they are also expensive. PVC pipe is cheaper, but not as strong. Any PVC pipe used should be U/V resistant so that the sun's rays don't deteriorate the material. One possible material that is free for the taking in some parts of the country is bamboo. When picking out bamboo, pick thick straight pieces that have no cracked places. Bamboo should be weatherproofed by filling the ends and any cracks with caulking, and then painting the whole thing with varnish or marine paint. Bamboo should be roughed up first to allow the sealer to soak in, using roughing sandpaper. Apply at least two coats of varnish.

Step 2. Cut angle aluminum into 3 ft. sections. Drill 2 holes in each piece, one hole 1½" on either side of exact center. These holes must be big enough to fit the U-Bolts through.

Step 3. Clamp support arms in place on each piece of angle aluminum with hose clamps. If necessary, use rubber padding in between clamps and arms for a snug fit. Leave a 6-inch gap between pieces for U-bolting the cross-arms to the boom. The distance from tip to tip on each cross-arm should be the following:

Reflector	2 cross-arms	13'8"
Driven	2 cross-arms	13'2"
Director	2 cross-arms	12'8"

Keep the cross-arms for each element separate.

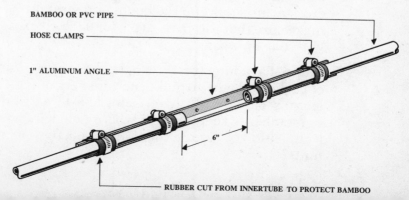

Fig. 11-21 Cross arm dimensions

BAMBOO OR PVC PIPE

HOSE CLAMPS

1" ALUMINUM ANGLE

6"

RUBBER CUT FROM INNERTUBE TO PROTECT BAMBOO

Step 4. Making an assembly stand. You'll need to mount the boom up off the ground at least 6½ feet to allow you to put on the cross-arms. This will give you room to spin the quad around while putting on the wires. That lets you be on the ground for that part of the assembly, a much easier way of doing it than being up in the air. What we did was take two saw horses and nail an upright to each one. We nailed in a couple of 16-penny nails in the top of each one. The resulting notches provided cradles for the boom.

Also, it's a good idea to assemble the quad as near as possible to where it is to be mounted. That will make it much easier to get it up there when the time comes.

Fig. 11-22 Quad installation

Step 5. Mounting cross-arms on the boom. After getting the boom up in the air, you can U-bolt on the cross-arms for each element. The pair of cross-arms the right length to make up each element are placed back to back, making the X pattern that supports the wire square that is the element. The U-bolts go around the boom and through the holes in each piece of angle aluminum. It's a good idea to have a little piece of rubber in between the boom and the U-bolts to prevent any slippage caused by the metal-on-metal contact. Torque  down the U-bolt nuts as tightly as possible while keeping the cross-arms square to the boom and straight up and down. Also make sure that the cross-arms for each element line up straight with one another.

Step 6. Fastening the wire to the cross-arms. First, you'll need to cut a piece of wire to make each element out of. Cut the following lengths of wire: 38'1"-reflector; 36'11"-driven; 35'9"-director. Remember to keep straight where each wire goes so as to get the right length of wire on the right set of cross-arms. **This is important!**

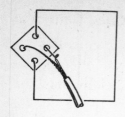

Fig. 11-23 Feed connection

The wire can be tied down on the ends of the support arms a few inches from the ends of the tips with several tight turns of nylon string. Keep the wires tightly strung between the cross-arms without any kinks, loops, or slack. This can be done while standing on the ground and rotating the cross-arms around from top to bottom while fastening on the wire, until you have made a square. All four sides of each element's square radiator should be equal in length.

String the wires for the driven element so that the two ends are in the middle, between the two spreaders. Now twist the two ends of the reflector together. Make sure to scrape any insulation or enamel off the wires and solder the connection. Do the same for the director.

Make sure not to cut any of the wires off when connecting the ends together. Twist together only two inches of each end. Don't connect the wires of the driven element together yet.

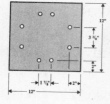

Fig. 11-24 Plate dimensions

Step 7. Hooking up the driven element. Connect each end of the driven element into opposite holes of the plexiglass. This is done by making a loop through the hole and twisting the wire back on itself. Now attach some RG58 or RG8 coax to the driven element's wires.

Strip back the coax about 3 to 4 inches and attach the inner conductor of the coax to the end that will be the top of the antenna. Connect the shield side of the coax to the other end of the driven element. Twist together, solder, and tape each connection.

Step 8: Mast to boom mount. Drill the holes in the aluminum or steel plate according to the diagram. Make sure holes are big enough for the U-bolts to fit through. The two U-bolts that attach to the mast will have to be the same size as the mast's diameter. Now mount the plate on the boom at the balance point of the antenna. It should be just behind the driven element. These bolts should be tightened down securely, using lock washers.

The antenna can now be mounted on the tower or pole. The mast is used between the rotator and the boom.

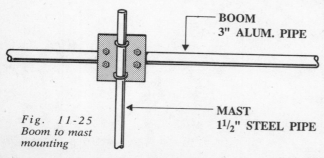

BOOM
3" ALUM. PIPE

MAST
1½" STEEL PIPE

Fig. 11-25 Boom to mast mounting

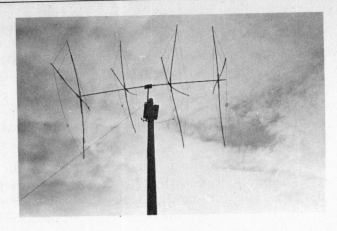

*Fig. 11-26
Four element
quad*

Quad Gain

2 elements
9 dB

3 elements
12 dB

4 elements
14 dB

5 elements
17 dB

Make sure you check your SWR before settling down to operate. It should be lower than 2. All the ones we've built have had an SWR of 1.5 or better. Be sure you've mounted your antenna, and it's not still on the ground when you check the SWR.

Quads are somewhat more susceptible to damage from high winds than other antennas and should be as tightly assembled as possible for long-lasting performance.

You can make this quad with two elements, also. The boom would only have to be 6 feet long. Just leave off the director and mount the driven element and reflector on two opposite ends of the boom. The mast-to-boom plate would be mounted on the center of the boom at the balance point. This antenna is physically much smaller, while only sacrificing about 3 dB gain. You could also make a higher gain quad by adding more directors and having a longer boom, just so you space them the same as you spaced the other director from the driven element. This makes for a longer, bigger antenna.

Ear Trouble!

*Fig. 11-27 Big
Bertha beam*

Chapter Twelve

How Far Can My CB Radio Talk?
(The CB Fanatic's Guide to Getting Out)

This is the most asked question from CB radio operators around the world. Obviously the answer to this question depends on a number of factors. What follows are ten questions that you should ask yourself concerning your present CB radio system. Each question concerns one of the basic factors of CB communications.

1. How much power does your CB radio put out?
The more power that your CB radio puts out, the farther away you can be heard.

2. How high and clear of obstacles is your antenna?
The higher that the antenna is and the clearer shot that you have toward the desired direction of communication, the better. This makes a definite difference in both the transmission and reception of signals. Mobiles get out best from a higher elevation.

3. What kind of mike are you using?
On AM CB rigs, a power mike can increase your modulation. The closer your modulation is to 100%, the better. On FM CB radios a power mike might help, but could also make your signal sound worse. On SSB rigs, a speech compressor micro-

phone can increase the amount of average power that your
radio is transmitting.

4. How is your SWR?

The closer that your antenna is to a 1:1 SWR, the better. This is
an indication of how well your radio and coaxial line is
matched to your antenna. A good match indicates an efficient
use of the power transmitted.

5. How much gain does your antenna have?

A gain antenna makes more effective use of the transmitted
signal, shaping and directing it for the most optimum performance. The higher the gain of an antenna, the more Effective Radiated Power produced from your station.

6. How much of your transmitted power is reaching the antenna?

Losses in the coax can dissipate some of your signal. To cut
down on this loss, have your radio as close to the antenna as is
practical. The thicker RG-8 coax has less line loss than the
skinnier RG-58. Each connector in your coaxial line will cause
you to lose as much as 1 dB of signal. This is true for any meter,
coaxial switch or other add-on device: any interruption in the
coax will cause you to lose a little.

7. What kind of antenna polarization are you using?

For local communications, vertical polarization generally
works best. DX communications can utilize either polarization, with horizontal sometimes offering the advantage of
limiting interference from local stations.

8. What mode of communications are you using?

On SSB, your range of communications will be more than
twice as effective per watt of power than an AM signal would
be. With FM, local communications are superior to AM signals because of increased clarity and less susceptibility to
noise and static. So far there are few DX stations operating
FM—a definite limiting factor.

9. What time is it?

The time of day, of the year and of the 11 year sunspot cycle all
directly affect our ability to communicate. Local contacts are
often severely limited by high-level signals skipping in from
other parts of the world. For best local communications, it is
essential to select the correct time, when skip conditions are

at a minimum. Amateur radio operators have found that DX communications, on the other hand, can only take place during the times when the atmospheric conditions are favorable.

10. What channel are you on?

Obviously, the clearer the channel that you are on, the further that you can communicate. This is equally true for both local and DX communications. Also, if you are operating on SSB or FM, it is important to be using channels that others operating these modes will be listening to. When skip conditions are good, it is difficult to locate a clear space anywhere within the American 40 channels, because so many stations around the world are operating simultaneously. That is why CBers in many parts of the world now operate in broad sections of frequencies above and below the American CB band. They are looking for a little peace and quiet. The British FM CB channels are in the area above the regular AM channels.

The better your station is, the more opportunities you will have for achieving the maximum range of communications. So it's really up to you—the sky's the limit!

APPENDICES

Appendix A:
CB Citizen's Band Radio Service Rules 95.401

Prepared by the Federal Communications Commission
Washington, D.C.

Effective: **June 3, 1983**

Subpart D–Citizens Band (CB) Radio Service

General Provisions

§95.401 (CB Rule 1) What is the Citizens Band (CB) Radio Service?

The CB Radio Service is a private, two-way, short distance voice communications service for personal or business activities. The CB Radio Service may also be used for voice paging.

§95.402 (CB Rule 2) How do I use these rules?

(a) You must comply with these rules (See CB Rule 21 §95.421, for the penalties for violations) when you operate a station in the CB Service from:

(1) Within or over the territorial limits of places where radio services are regulated by the FCC (see rule 5, §95.405);

(2) Aboard any vessel or aircraft registered in the United Sates; OR

(3) Aboard any unregistered vessel or aircraft owned or operated by a United States citizen or company.

(b) Your CB station must comply with technical rules found in Subpart E of part 95.

(c) Where the rules use the word "you", "you" means a person operating a CB station

(d) Where the rules use the word "person", the rules are concerned with an individual, a corporation, a partnership, an association, a joint stock company, a trust, a state, territorial or local government unit, of other legal entity.

(e) Where the rules use the term "FCC", that means the Federal Communications Commission.

(f) Where the rules use the term "CB station", that means a radio station transmitting in the CB Radio Service.

§95.403 (CB Rule 3) Am I eligible to operate a CB station?

You are authorized to operate a CB station unless:

(a) You are a foreign government, a representative of a foreign government, or a federal government agency; OR

(b) The FCC has issued a cease and desist order to you, and the order is still in effect.

§95.404 (CB Rule 4) Do I need a license?

You do not need an individual license to operate a CB station. You are authorized by this rule to operate your CB station in accordance with the rules in this subpart.

§95.405 (CB Rule 5) Where may I operate my CB station?

You are authorized to operate your CB station from:

(a) Within or over any area of the world where radio services are regulated by the FCC. Those areas are within the territorial limits of:

(1) The fifty United States.

(2) The District of Columbia.

Caribbean Insular areas

(3) Commonwealth of Puerto Rico.

(4) Navassa Island.

(5) United States Virgin Islands (50 Islets and cays).

Pacific Insular areas

(6) American Samoa (seven islands).

(7) Baker Island.

(8) Commonwealth of Northern Mariana Islands.

(9) Guam Island.

(10) Howland Island.

(11) Jarvis Island.

(12) Johnston Island (Islets East, Johnston, North and Sand).

(13) Kingsman Reef.

(14) Midway Island (Islets Eastern and Sand).

(15) Palmyra Island (more than 50 islets).

(16) Wake Island (Islets Peale, Wake and Wilkes).

(b) Any other area of the world, except within the territorial limits of areas where radio services are regulated by –

(1) An agency of the United States other than the FCC. (You are subject to its rules.)

(2) Any foreign government. (You are subject to its rules.)

(c) An aircraft or ship, with the permission of the captain, within or over any area of the world where radio services are regulated by the FCC or upon or over international waters. You must operate your CB station according to any applicable treaty to which the United States is a party.

§95.406   (CB Rule 6) Are there any special restrictions on the location of my CB station?

(a) If your CB station is located on premises controlled by the Department of Defense you may be required to comply with additional regulations imposed by the commanding officer of the installation.

(b) If your CB station will be constructed on land of environmental or historical importance (such as a location significant in American history, architecture or culture), you may be required to provide information and to comply with §§ 1.1305 through 1.1319 of the FCC's Rules.

How To Operate a CB Station

§ 95.407   (CB Rule 7) On what channels may I operate?

(a) Your CB station may transmit only on the following channels (frequencies):

Channel	Frequency (MegaHertz, MHz)	Channel	Frequency (Megahertz MHz)
1	26.965	21	27.215
2	26.975	22	27.225
3	26.985	23	27.255
4	27.005	24	27.235
5	27.015	25	27.245
6	27.025	26	27.265
7	27.035	27	27.275
8	27.055	28	27.285
9	27.065	29	27.295
10	27.075	30	27.305
11	27.085	31	27.315
12	27.105	32	27.325
13	27.115	33	27.335
14	27.125	34	27.345
15	27.135	35	27.355
16	27.155	36	27.365
17	27.165	37	27.375
18	27.175	38	27.385
19	27.185	39	27.395
20	27.205	40	27.405

(b) Channel 9 may be used only for emergency communications or for traveler assistance.

(c) You must, at all times and on all channels, give priority to emergency communication messages concerning the immediate safety of life or the immediate protection of property.

(d) You may use any channel for emergency communications or for traveler assistance.

(e) You must share each channel with other users.

(f) The FCC will not assign any channel for the private or exclusive use of any particular CB station or group of stations.

(g) The FCC will not assign any channel for the private or exclusive use of CB stations transmitting single sideband (SSB) or AM.

§95.408 (CB Rule 8) How high may I put my antenna?

(a) "Antenna means the radiating system (for transmitting, receiving or both) and the structure holding it up (tower, pole or mast). It also means everything else attached to the radiating system and the structure.

(b) If your antenna is mounted on a hand-held portable unit, none of the following limitations apply.

(c) If your antenna is installed at a fixed location it (whether receiving, transmitting or both) must comply with either one of the following:

    (1) The highest point must not be more than 6.10 meters (20 feet) higher than the highest point of the building or tree on which it is mounted; OR

    (2) The highest point must not be more than 16.3 meters (60 feet) above the ground.

(d) If your CB station is located near an airport, and if your antenna structure is more than 6.1 meters (20 feet) high, you may have to obey additional restrictions. The highest point of your antenna must not exceed one meter above the airport elevation for every hundred meters of distance from the nearest airport runway. Differences in ground elevation between your antenna and the airport runway may complicate this formula. If your CB station is near an airport, you may contact the nearest FCC field office for a worksheet to help you figure the maximum allowable height for your antenna. Consult Part 17 of the FCC's Rules for more information.

WARNING: Installation and removal of CB Station Antennas near power lines is dangerous. For your safety follow the installation directions included with your antenna.

§95.409 (CB Rule 9) What equipment may I use at my CB station?

(a) You must use an FCC type-accepted CB transmitter at your CB station. You can identify an FCC type-accepted transmitter by the type-acceptance label placed on it by the manufacturer. You may examine a list of type-accepted equipment at any FCC Field Office or at FCC Headquarters. Use of a transmitter which is not FCC type-accepted voids your authority to operate the station.

(b) You must not make, or have made, any internal modification to a type-accepted CB transmitter. (See CB Rule 25 §95.425). Any internal modification to a type-accepted CB transmitter cancels the type-acceptance, and use of such a transmitter voids your authority to operate the station.

§95.410   (CB Rule 10) How much power may I use?

(a) Your CB station transmitter power output must not exceed the following values under any conditions:

AM (A3) - 4 watts (carrier power)
SSB - 12 watts (peak envelope power)

(b) If you need more information about the power rule, see the technical rules in Subpart E of Part 95.

(c) Use of a transmitter which has carrier or peak envelope power in excess of that authorized voids your authority to operate the station.

§95.411   (CB Rule 11) May I use power amplifiers?

(a) You may not attach the following items (power amplifiers) to your type-accepted CB transmitter in any way:
  (1) External radio frequency (RF) power amplifiers (sometimes called linears or linear amplifiers): OR
  (2) Any other devices which, when used with a radio transmitter as a signal source, are capable of amplifying the signal.

(b) There are no exceptions to this rule and use of a power amplifier voids your authority to operate the station.

(c) The FCC will presume you have used a linear or other external RF power amplifier if —
  (1) It is in your possession or on your premises; AND
  (2) There is other evidence that you have operated your CB station with more power than allowed by CB Rule 10, §95.410.

(d) Paragraph (c) of this section does not apply if you hold a license in another radio service which allows you to operate an external RF power amplifier.

§95.412 (CB Rule 12) What communications may be transmitted?

(a) You may use your CB station to transmit two-way plain language communications. Two-way plain language communications are communications without codes or coded messages. Operating signals such as "ten codes" are not considered codes or coded message. You may transmit two-way plain language communications only to other CB stations, to units of your own CB station or to authorized government stations on CB frequencies about —

(1) Your personal or business activities or those of members of your immediate family living in your hosehold;

(2) Emergencies (see CB Rule 18 §95.418);

(3) Traveler assistance (see CB Rule 18, §95.418); or

(4) Civil defense activities in connection with official tests or drills conducted by, or actual emergencies announced by, the civil defense agency with authority over the area in which your station is located.

(b) You may use your CB station to transmit a tone signal only when the signal is used to make contact or to continue communications. (Examples of circuits using these signals are tone-operated squelch and selective calling circuits.) If the signal is an audible tone, it must last no longer than 15 seconds at one time. If the signal is a sub-audible tone, it may be transmitted continuously only as long as you are talking.

(c) You may use your CB station to transmit one-way communications (messages which are not intended to establish communications between two or more particular CB stations) only for emergency communications, traveler assistance, brief tests (radio checks) or voice paging.

§95.413 (CB Rule 13) What communications are prohibited?

(a) You may not use a CB station —

(1) In connection with any activity which is against federal state or local law;

(2) To transmit obscene, indecent or profane words, language or meaning;

(3) To interfere intentionally with the communications of another CB station;

(4) To transmit one-way communications, except for emergency communications, traveler assistance, brief tests (radio checks), or voice paging;

(5) To advertise or solicit the sale of any goods or services;

(6) To transmit music, whistling, sound effects or any material to amuse or entertain;

(7) To transmit any sound effect solely to attract attention;

(8) To transmit the word "MAYDAY" or any other international distress signal, except when your station is located in a ship, aircraft or other vehicle which is threatened by grave and imminent danger and you are requesting immediate assistance;

(9) To communicate with, or attempt to communicate with, any CB station more than 250 kilometers (155.3 miles) away;

(10) To advertise a political candidate or political campaign; (you may use your CB radio for the business or organizational

aspects of a campaign if you follow all other applicable rules);

(11) To communicate with stations in other countries, except General Radio Service stations in Canada; or

(12) To transmit a false or deceptive communication.

(b) You must not use a CB station to transmit communications for live or delayed rebroadcast on a radio or television broadcast station. You may use your CB station to gather news items or to prepare programs.

§95.414   (CB Rule 14) May I be paid to use my CB station?

(a) You may not accept direct or indirect payment for transmitting with a CB station.

(b) You may use a CB station to help you provide a service and be paid for that service, as long as you are paid only for the service and not for the actual use of the CB station.

§95.415   (CB Rule 15) Who is responsible for communications I make?

You are responsible for all communications which are made by you from a CB station.

§95.416   (CB Rule 16) Do I have to limit the length of my communications?

(a) You must limit your CB communications to the minimum practical time.

(b) If you are communicating with another CB station or stations, you, and the stations communicating with you, must limit each of your conversations to no more than five continuous minutes.

(c) At the end of your conversation, you, and the stations communicating with you, must not transmit again for at least one minute.

§95.417   (CB Rule 17) Do I identify my CB communications?

(a) You need not identify your CB communications

(b) You are encouraged to identify your CB communications by any or the following means:

(1) Previously assigned CB call sign;

(2) K prefix followed by operator initials and residence zip code;

(3) Name; OR

(4) Organizational description including name and any applicable operator unit number

(c) You are encouraged to use your "handle" only in conjunction with the methods of identification listed in paragraph (b) of this section.

§95.418 (CB Rule 18) How do I use my CB station in an emergency or to assist a traveler?

(a) You must at all times and on all channels, give priority to emergency communications.

(b) When you are directly participating in emergency communications, you do not have to comply with the rule about the length of transmissions (CB Rule 16 §95.416). You must obey all other rules.

(c) You may use your CB station for communications necessary to assist a traveler to reach a destination or to receive necessary services. When you are using your CB station to assist a traveler, you do not have to obey the rule about length of transmissions (CB Rule 16, §95.416). You must obey all other rules.

§95.419 (CB Rule 19) May I operate my CB transmitter by remote control?

(a) You may not operate a CB station transmitter by radio remote control.

(b) You may operate a CB transmitter by wireless remote control if you obtain specific approval in writing from the FCC. To obtain FCC approval, you must show why you need to operate your station by wireless remote control. Send your request and justification to FCC, Gettysburg, PA 17325. If you receive FCC approval, you must keep the approval as part of your earth station record. (See CB Rule 27, §95.427).

§95.420 (CB Rule 20) May I connect my CB transmitter to a telephone?

(a) You may connect your CB station transmitter to a telephone if you can comply with all of the following:

(1) You or someone else must be present at your CB station and must—

(i) Manually make the connection (the connection must not be made by remote control);

(ii) Supervise the operation of the transmitter during the connection;

(iii) Listen to each communication during the connection; AND

(iv) Stop all communications if there are operations in violation of these rules.

(2) Each communication during the telephone connection must comply with all of these rules.

(3) You must obey any restriction that the telephone company places on the connection of a CB transmitter to a telephone.

(b) The CB transmitter you connect to a telephone must not be shared with any other CB station.

(c) If you connect your CB transmitter to a telephone, you must use a phone patch device which has been registered with the FCC.

Other Things You need to Know

§95.421   (CB Rule 21) What are the penalties for violating these rules?

(a) If the FCC finds that you have willfully or repeatedly violated the Communications Act or the FCC rules, you may have to pay as much as $2,000 for each violation, up to a total of $5,000. (See section 503(b) of the Communications Act.)

(b) If the FCC finds that you have violated any section of the Communications Act or the FCC rules, you may be ordered to stop whatever action caused the violation [See Section 312(b) of the Communications Act.]

(c) If a federal court finds that you have willfully and knowingly violated any FCC Rule, you may be fined up to $500 for each day you committed the violation. (See Section 502 of the Communications Act.)

(d) If a federal court finds that you have willfully and knowingly violated any provision of the Communications Act, you may be fined up to $10,000 or you may be imprisoned for one year, or both. (See Section 501 of the Communications Act).

§95.422   (CB Rule 22) How do I answer correspondence from the FCC?

(a) If it appears to the FCC that you have violated the Communications Act or these rules, the FCC may send you a discrepancy notice.

(b) Within the time period stated in the notice, you must answer with:

(1) A complete written statement about the apparent discrepancy;

(2) A complete written statement about any action you have taken to correct the apparent violation and to prevent it from happening again; AND

(3) The name of the person operating at the time of the apparent violation.

(c) If the FCC sends you a letter asking you questions about your CB radio station or its operation, you must answer each of the questions with a complete written statement within the time period stated in the letter.

(d) You must not shorten your answer by references to other communication or notices.

(e) You must send your answer to the FCC office which sent you the notice.

(f) You must keep a copy of your answer in your stations records (See CB Rule 27, §95.427).

§95.423 (CB Rule 23) What must I do if the FCC tells me that my CB station is causing interference?

(a) If the FCC tells you that your CB station is causing interference for technical reasons you must follow all instructions in the official FCC notice. (This notice may require you to have technical adjustments made to your equipment.

(b) You must comply with any restricted hours of CB station operation which may be included in the official notice.

§95.424 (CB Rule 24) How do I have my CB station transmitter serviced?

(a) You may adjust an antenna to your CB transmitter and you may make radio checks. (A radio check means a one way transmission for a short time in order to test the transmitter.)

(b) Each internal repair and each internal adjustment to your FCC type-accepted CB transmitter (See CB Rule 9, §95.409) must be made by or under the direct supervision of a person licensed by the FCC as a General Radiotelephone Operator.

(c) Except as provided in paragraph (d) of this section, each internal repair and each internal adjustment of a CB transmitter in which signals are transmitted must be made using a nonradiating ("dummy") antenna.

(d) Brief test signals (signals not longer than one minute during any five minute period) using a radiating antenna may be transmitted in order to;

    (1) Adjust an antenna to a transmitter;

    (2) Detect or measure radiation of energy other than the intended signal; OR

    (3) Tune a receiver to your CB transmitter.

§95.425 (CB Rule 25) May I make any changes to my CB station transmitter?

(a) You must not make or have any one else make any internal modification to your CB transmitter.

(b) Internal modification does not include:

    (1) Repair or servicing of a CB transmitter (see CB Rule 24, §95.424); OR

    (2) Changing plug-in modules which were type accepted as part of your CB transmitter.

(c) You must not operate a CB transmitter which has been modified by any one in any way, including modification to operate on un-authorized frequencies or with illegal power. (See CB Rules 9 and 11, §95.409 and §95.411)

§95.426 (CB Rule 26) Do I have to make my CB station available for inspection?

(a) If an authorized FCC representative requests to inspect your CB station, you must make your CB station and records available for inspection.

(b) A CB station includes all of the radio equipment you use.

§95.427 (CB Rule 27) What are my station records?

Your station records include the following documents, as applicable:

(a) A copy of each response to an FCC violation notice or and FCC letter (See CB Rule 22, §95.422)

(b) Each written permission received from the FCC (See Rule 19, §95.419)

§95.428 (CB Rule 28) How do I contact the FCC?

(a) Write to your nearest FCC Field Office if you:

(1) Want to report an interference complaint; OR

(2) Want to know if the FCC has type-accepted a transmitter for CB.

(b) Write to the FCC Private Radio Bureau, Personal Radio Branch, Washington, DC 20554 if you have questions about the CB Rules.

9. Paragraph (f) of §95.645 of the rules is revised to read:

§95.645 Additional requirements for type acceptance

(f) A copy of Subpart D or part 95 of the Commission's Rules, to be current at the time of packing of the transmitter, shall be furnished with each transmitter.

REPRINTED FROM:

Federal Register   Vl. 48, No. 108   Friday, June 3, 1983

Rules and Regulations

Appendix B:

U.K. Home Office
Radio Regulatory Department
CB Performance Specifications

Angle modulated 27 MHz radio equipment for use in the Citizens Band Radio Service.

Foreword

1. Citizen's Band radio, a personal two-way radio system, is available for use throughout the United Kingdom. It operates in the 27 MHz and the 934 MHz bands.

2. The Wireless Telegraphy Act of 1949 provides that no radio equipment may be installed or used except under the authority of the Secretary of State. All citizens band radio equipment, whether hand held, mobile or base station, must be covered by a licence; it is a condition of this that the aparatus fulfills, and is maintained to, certain minimum technical standards. This specification sets out these standards for 27 MHz FM equipment; 934 MHz FM equipment is subject to a separate specification.

3. The manufacturer, assembler or importer of citizens band equipment is responsible for ensuring that the apparatus conforms with the specification; and any additional requirements imposed by regulations under the Wireless Telegraphy Act of 1949. Conformity with the required standards may be established by tests carried out by the manufacturer, assembler or importer, or by a reputable test establishment acting on his behalf, but in either case conformity with the specification will remain the responsibility of the manufacturer, assembler or importer.

1. General

1.1 Scope of Specification

This specification covers the minimum performance requirements for angle-modulated radio equipments, comprising base station, mobile and hand-held tramsmitters and receivers or receivers only and additionally any accessories, for example attenuators or vehicle adaptors for optional use with the above for use in the Citizens Band Radio Service. For all equipment covered by this specification, the nominal separation between adjacent channel carrier frequencies is 10 KHz.

1.2 Permitted effective radiated power.

The output radio frequency power of the equipment is limited to 4 W. With the antenna permitted by the conditions of the licence for use with the equipment this gives an effective radiated power of 2 W. (See note *)
If an antenna is mounted at a height exceeding 7 meters, the licence will require a reduction in transmitter power of 10 dB.
To enable the user to accomplish this easily the equipment manufacturer should provide as a standard facility on the equipment means by which the transmitter output power may be reduced by a minimum of 10 dB.

1.3 Operating frequencies

The equipment shall provide for transmissions and reception only of angle modulated emissions on one or more of the following radio frequency channels:

	Frequency		Frequency
Channel 1	27.60126 MHz	Channel 21	27.80125 MHz
Channel 2	27.61125 MHz	Channel 22	27.81125 MHz
Channel 3	27.62125 MHz	Channel 23	27.82125 MHz
Channel 4	27.63125 MHz	Channel 24	27.83125 MHz
Channel 5	27.64125 MHz	Channel 25	27.84125 MHz
Channel 6	27.65125 MHz	Channel 26	27.85125 MHz
Channel 7	27.66125 MHz	Channel 27	27.86125 MHz
Channel 8	27.67125 MHz	Channel 28	27.87125 MHz
Channel 9	27.68125 MHz	Channel 29	27.88125 MHz
Channel 10	27.69125 MHz	Channel 30	27.89125 MHz
Channel 11	27.70125 MHz	Channel 31	27.90125 MHz
Channel 12	27.71125 MHz	Channel 32	27.91125 MHz
Channel 13	27.72125 MHz	Channel 33	27.92125 MHz
Channel 14	27.73125 MHz	Channel 34	27.93125 MHz
Channel 15	27.74125 MHz	Channel 35	27.94125 MHz
Channel 16	27.75125 MHz	Channel 36	27.95125 MHz
Channel 17	27.76125 MHz	Channel 37	27.96125 MHz
Channel 18	27.77125 MHz	Channel 38	27.97125 MHz
Channel 19	27.78125 MHz	Channel 39	27.98125 MHz
Channel 20	27.79125 MHz	Channel 40	27.99125 MHz

Citizens band radio equipment shall not contain facilities for transmissions of radio frequencies other than those listed above, and those contained in MPT 1321. Single channel equipment may be tested on any one of the approved channels. Multi-channel equipment shall be equipped to operate at the center,

*Note: The licence requires that equipments which have provision for the connection of an external antenna shall not be connected to other than a single element rod or wire antenna not exceeding 1.5 N in overall length.

and the upper and lower limits of the frequency range over which channel switching is possible.

1.4 Permitted modulation

Only equipment which employs angle modulation and has no facilities for any other form of modulation will meet the requirements of this specification.

1.5 Labelling

This equipment shall be provided with a clear indication of the type number and name of the manufacturer.

1.6 Certification of Compliance

Compliance with this specification shall be indicated by an authorized mark stamped or engraved on the front panel of the equipment. The mark used to indicate compliance shall be as shown in Fig. 1.

Figure 1
Letter and figure height not less that 2 mm

1.7 Controls

Those controls, which if maladjusted might increase the interfering potentialities of the equipment, shall not be easily accessible.

2. Test conditions: atmospheric conditions and power supplies

2.1 General

Tests shall be made under normal test conditions (Clause 2.3) and also, where stated, under extreme test conditions (Clause 2.4).

2.2 Test power source

During tests, the power supply for the equipment may be replaced by a test power source, capable of producing normal and extreme test voltages as specified in Clauses 2.3.2 and 2.4.2. The internal impedance of the test power source shall be low enough for its effect on the test results to be negligible. For the purposes of tests, the voltage of the power supply shall be measured at the input terminals of the equipment. During the tests of the power source, voltage shall be maintained within a tolerance of ± 3% relative to the voltage at the beginning of each test. In equipment in which batteries are incorporated, the test power source shall be applied as close to the battery terminals as practicable.

2.3 Normal test conditions

2.3.1 Normal temperature and humidity

The normal temperature and humidity conditions for tests shall be any convenient combination of temperature and humidity within the following ranges:

Temperature 15°C to 35°C
Relative humidity 20% to 75%

When it is impracticable to carry out the tests under the conditions stated above,
a note to this effect stating the actual temperature and relative humidity during
the tests shall be added to the test report.

2.3.2 Normal test source voltage

2.3.2.1 Mains voltage

The normal voltage for equipment to be connected to the mains shall be the
nominal mains voltage. For the purpose of this specification, the nominal voltage
shall be the declared voltage or any of the declared voltages for which the
equipment was designed. The frequency of the test power source corresponding
to the AC mains shall be between 49 and 51 Hz.

2.3.2.2 Regulated lead-acid battery power sources

When the radio equipment is intended for operation from the usual type of
regulated lead-acid battery source, the normal test source voltage shall be 1.1
times the nominal voltage of the battery (6 volts, 12 volts, etc.)

2.3.3 Other power sources

For operations from other power sources or types of battery, either primary or
secondary, the normal test source voltage shall be that declared by the equipment manufacturer.

2.4 Extreme test conditions

2.4.1 Extreme temperatures

For tests at extreme temperatures, measurements shall be made in accordance
with the procedures specified in Clause 2.5 at an upper value of +45° C and at a
lower value of −5°C.

2.4.2 Extreme test source voltages

2.4.2.1 Mains voltage

The extreme test source voltages for equipment to be connected to an AC mains source shall be the nominal mains voltage ± 10%. The frequency of the test power source shall be between 49 and 51 Hz.

2.4.2.2 Regulated lead-acid battery power sources

When equipment is intended for operation from the usual type of regulated lead-acid power source, the extreme test voltages shall be 1.3 and 0.9 times the nominal voltage of the battery.

2.4.3 Other power sources

The lower extreme test voltage for equipment with power sources using primary batteries shall be as follows: (a) For Leclanche type of battery − 085 times the nominal voltage. (b) For mercury type of battery − 0.9 times the nominal voltage. (c) For other types of primary batteries − end point voltage declared by the equipment manufacturer.

For equipment using other power sources or capable of being operated from a variety of power sources, the extreme test voltages shall be those declared by the equipment manufacturer and shall be recorded with the test results.

2.5 Procedure for tests at extreme temperatures

2.5.1 General

Before making measurements, the equipment shall be placed in a temperature-controlled chamber for a period of one hour or for such period as may be judged necessary for thermal balance to be obtained. The equipment shall be switched off during the temperature stabilization period. The sequence of tests shall be chosen and the humidity content in the test chamber shall be controlled so that excessive condensation does not occur.

2.5.2 Test procedure

For tests at the upper temperature, after thermal balance has been attained (Clause 2.5.1), the equipment shall be switched on for 1 minute in the transmit condition after which the appropriate tests shall be carried out.

3. Electrical test conditions

3.1 Transmitter artificial load

Tests on the transmitter shall be carried out using a 50-ohm non-reactive load connected to the antenna terminals. If necessary, an impedance matching device may be used for testing.

3.2 Test Fixture

3.2.1 General

A test fixture will be required to permit relative measurements to be made on the sample*.

This test fixture shall preferably provide a 50 ohm radio frequency terminal at the working frequencies of the equipment. The test fixture shall provide input and output audio coupling and a means of connecting an external power supply. The following characteristics shall apply to the test fixture: (a) The coupling loss shall be as low as possible, and in any case not greater the 30 dB. (b) The variation of coupling loss with frequency shall not cause errors in measurement exceeding 2 dB: (c) The coupling device shall not incorporate any non-linear elements.

3.3 Test site and general arrangements for measurements involving the use of radiated fields

3.3.1 Test site

The test site shall be located on a surface or ground which is reasonably level. At one point of the site, a ground plane of at least 5 meters in diameter shall be provided. In the middle of this ground plane, a non- conducting support, capable of rotation through 360° in the horizontal plane, shall be used to support the test sample at 1.5 meters above the ground plane. The test site shall be large enough to allow the erection of a measuring or transmitting antenna at a distance from the test sample of not less than half the wavelength corresponding to the lower frequency to be considered. The distance actually used shall be recorded with the results of the tests carried out on the site. Sufficient precautions shall be taken to ensure that reflections from extraneous objects adjacent to the site, and ground reflections do not degrade the measurements.

3.3.2 Test antenna

The test antenna is used to detect the radiation from both the test sample and the substitution antenna, when the site is used for radiation measurements. This antenna is mounted on a support capable of allowing the antenna to be used either horizontally or vertically polarized and for the height of its center above ground to be varied over the range 1-5 meters. Preferably a test antenna with

---

*Note: Any connections provided on the equipment in order to facilitate relative measurements, shall not affect the performance of the equipment either in the test fixture or when making measurements involving the use of radiated fields.

pronounced directibility should be used. The size of the test antenna along the measurement axis shall not exceed 20% of the measuring distance. For radiation measurements, the test antenna is connected to a test receiver, capable of being tuned to any frequency under investigation and to measure accurately the relative levels of signals at its input.

3.3.3 Substitution Antenna

The substitution antenna shall be a ½ wavelength dipole resonant at the frequency under consideration, or a shortened dipole, calibrated against the ½ wavelength dipole. The center of this antenna shall coincide with the reference point of the test sample it has replaced. This reference point shall be the point at which the external antenna is connected. This distance between the lower extremity of the dipole and the ground shall be at least 0.3 meters.

The substitution antenna shall be connected to a calibrated signal generator when the site is used for radiation measurements. This signal generator and the receiver shall be operating at the frequencies under investigation and shall be connected through suitable matching and balancing networks.

3.4 Normal test modulation

Where stated, the transmitter shall have normal test modulation as follows:

The modulation frequency shall be 1 kHz and the resulting frequency deviation shall be 60% of the maximum permissible frequency deviation (Clause 4.3.1).

4. Transmitter

4.1 Frequency Error

4.1.1 Definition

The frequency error of the transmitter is the difference between the measured carrier frequency and its nominal value.

4.1.2 Method of measurement

(a) The transmitter output in the case of equipment with an antenna terminal, shall be connected to an artificial load (Clause 3.1) and in the case of equipment incorporating integral antenna, shall be placed in the test fixture (Clause 3.2) connected to an artificial load. The transmitter shall be operated in accordance with the manufacturer's instructions to obtain normal output power.

(b) The emission shall be monitored by a frequency counter and the carrier frequency shall be measured in the absence of modulation.

(c) The measurement shall be made under normal test conditions (Clause 2.3) and repeated under extreme conditions (Clauses 2.4.1 and 2.4.2 applied simultaneously).

4.1.3 Limits

The frequency error, under both normal and extreme test conditions, or at any intermediate condition, shall not exceed ± 1.5 KHz. If for determining the transmitter frequency, use is made of a synthesizer and/or a phase-locked loop system, the transmitter shall be inhibited when synchronization is absent.

4.2 Carrier power

The equipment manufacturer shall provide as a standard accessory an attenuator having a minimum attenuation of 10 dB, or alternatively provide a switch which can be used to reduce the power by a minimum of 10 dB, for use where necessary, between the transmitter output and the antenna terminals of the equipment, a removable link may be necessary.

4.2.1 Definition

For the purpose of this specification, the carrier power shall be the value of the power of an unmodulated carrier at the output terminals of a transmitter. For equipment with an integral antenna, it is the maximum value of effective radiated power of an unmodulated carrier. The rated output power is the maximum value of the transmitter output power declared by the manufacturer, at which all the requirements of this specification are met.

4.2.2 Method of measurement (Terminal Power)

(a) The transmitter shall be connected to a test load equal to the impedance for which it is designed.

(b) With the transmitter operating without modulation in accordance with the manufacturers' instructions, the power delivered to the test load shall be measured.

(c) The measurement shall be made under normal test conditions (Clause 2.3) and repeated under extreme test conditions Clauses 2.4.1 and 2.4.2 applied simultaneously.

4.2.3 Radiated Power

4.2.3.1 Method of measurement under normal test conditions

(a) On the test site fulfilling the requirements of Clause 3.3, the equipment shall be placed on the support in the following position:

   (i) equipment with internal antennae shall be arranged with that axis vertical which is closest to vertical in normal use;

   (ii) for equipment with rigid external antennae, the antenna shall be vertical;

   (iii) for equipment with non-rigid external antennae, with the antenna extended vertically upwards by a non-conducting support.

(b) The transmitter shall be switched on, without modulation, and the test receiver shall be tuned to the frequency of the signal being measured.

(c) The test antenna shall be orientated for vertical polarization and shall be raised or lowered through the specified height angle until a maximum signal level is detected on the test receiver.*

(d) The transmitter shall then be rotated or lowered through 360° until the maximum signal level is received.

(e) The transmitter shall be replaced by the substitution antenna, as defined in Clause 3.3 and the test antenna raised or lowered as necessary to ensure that the maximum signal is still received.

(f) The input signal to the substitution antenna shall be adjusted in level until an equal or known related level to that detected from the transmitter is obtained in the test receiver.

(g) The carrier power is equal to the power supplied to the substitution antenna, increased by the known relationship if necessary.

(h) Steps (a) to (g) shall be repeated for any alternative integral antenna supplied by the manufacturer.

(j) A check shall be made at other planes of polarization to ensure that the value obtained above is the maximum. If larger values are obtained, this fact shall be recorded in the test report.

* Note: The maximum may be a lower value than the obtainable heights outside the specified range.

4.2.3.2 Method of measurement under extreme test conditions

(a) The equipment shall be placed in the test fixture (Clause 3.2) connected to the artificial load (Clause 3.1) with a means of measuring the power delivered to this load.

(b) In the absence of modulation, the transmitter shall be operated in accordance with the manufacturer's instructions. The carrier power shall then be measured.

(c) The measurement shall be made under normal test conditions (Clause 2.3) and repeated under extreme test conditions (Clauses 2.4.1 and 2.4 2 applied simultaneously).

4.2.4 Limits

The carrier power measured under normal test conditions in accordance with clause 4.2.2 shall not exceed 4 watts. The effective radiated power measured under normal test conditions in accordance with Clause 4.2.2 or Clause 4.2.3 whichever is applicable.

4.3 Frequency deviation

The frequency deviation is the difference between the instantaneous frequency of the modulated radio-frequency signal and the carrier frequency in the absence of modulation. For test purposes, only the maximum value of the frequency deviation available in the transmitter will be measured.

4.3.2 Maximum permissible frequency deviation

4.3.2.1 Definition

The maximum permissible frequency deviation is the maximum value of deviation under any conditions of modulation.

4.3.2.2 Method of measurement

(a) The equipment, if a fixed station, shall be connected to a test load equal to the impedance for which it was designed and if portable shall be placed in the test fixture. (Clause 3.2)

(b)The emission shall be monitored by a modulation meter capable of measuring the peak value of both positive and negative frequency deviation including that due to any harmonics and inter-modulation products which may be produced in the transmitter.

(c) The transmitter shall then be modulated by an audio frequency signal 20 dB above the level necessary to produce normal test modulation (Clause 3.4) and the modulation frequency varied from 300 Hz to 3 KHz.

(d) At each test frequency, the peak deviation shall be measured.

4.3.3 Limit

At any modulating frequency, the frequency deviation shall not exceed ± 2.5 kHz.

4.4 Adjacent channel power

4.4.1 Definition

The adjacent channel power is that part of the total power output of a transmitter under defined conditions of modulation, which falls within the bandwidth of a receiver of the type normally used in the system and operating on a channel either 10 KHz above or below the nominal frequency of the transmitter.

4.4.2 Method of measurement

For equipment with radio-frequency output terminals, this measurement shall be carried out at these terminals. For equipment with integral antennae, this measurement shall be carried out at the output of the test fixture.

(a) The equipment or the test fixture shall be connected to the power measuring receiver via a 50 ohm attenuator, set to produce an appropriate level at the receiver input.

(b) The transmitter shall be operated at the carrier wave measured under normal test conditions in clauses 4.2.2 or 4.2.3 as applicable.

(c) The transmitter shall be modulated at 1250 Hz at a level 20 dB greater than that required to produce 60% of the maximum permissible frequency deviation (Clause 4.3.1)

(d) The test receiver shall then be tuned to the nominal frequency of the transmitter and the receiver attenuator adjusted to a value 'p' such that a meter reading of the order of 5 dB above the receiver noise level is obtained.

(e) The test receiver shall then be tuned to the nominal frequency of the higher adapter channel and the receiver attenuator re-adjusted to a value 'q' such that the same meter reading is again obtained.

(f) The ratio, in decibels, of the adjacent channel power to the carrier power is the difference between the attenuator settings 'p' and 'q'.

(g) The adjacent channel power shall be determined by applying this ratio to the carrier power as determined in Clauses 4.2.2 or 4.2.3 as applicable.

(h) The measurement shall be repeated for the lower adjacent channel.

4.4.3 Limits

The adjacent channel power shall not exceed a value of 10 %µW.

4.4.4 Power measuring receiver specification

The power measuring receiver shall comprise a mixer, a crystal filter, a variable attenuator, an intermediate frequency amplifier, and a r.m.s. meter connected in cascade, using a low noise signal generator as a local oscillator.

The bandwidth of the filter shall be as follows (with a tolerance of ±10%):

Bandwidth between 6 dB attenuation points (kHz): 8.5

Bandwidth between 70 dB attenuation points (kHz): 17.5

Bandwidth between 90 dB attenuation points (kHz): 25

The attenuator shall cover a range of at least 80 dB in 1 dB steps. The noise factor of the amplifier shall be not worse than 4 dB. Over the 6 dB bandwidth, the amplitude/frequency characteristics of the amplifier shall not vary by more than 1 dB.

The combined response of the filter and amplifier outside the 90 dB bandwidth shall maintain an attenuation of at least 90 dB. The r.m.s. meter, if not a power meter, shall have a crest factor of at least 10 for the full scale readings. The measuring accuracy of the receiver over an input level range of 100 dB shall be better than 1.5 dB.

4.5 Spurious emissions

4.5.1 Definition

Spurious emissions are emissions at frequencies other than those of the carrier and sidebands associated with normal modulation. The level of spurious emissions shall be measured as:

(a) Their power level in a specified load, where the equipment is fitted with output terminals and (b) Their effective radiated power when radiated by an integral antenna or from the cabinet and chassis of the equipment.

4.5.2 Method of measurement - power level

(a) The transmitter output shall be connected to either a spectrum analyser via an attenuator, or an artificial load, with means of monitoring the emission with a spectrum analyser or selective voltmeter.

(b) The transmitter shall be unmodulated and at each spurious emission in the frequency range 100 kHz to 1000 MHz, the level of the emission shall be measured relative to the carrier emission.

(c) The power level of each emission shall be determined by applying the ratio measured to the carrier power level determined in Clause 4.2.3.

4.5.3 Method of measurement -effective radiated power.

(a) On a test site fulfilling the requirements of Clause 3.2 the transmitter shall be placed at the specified height on the support.

(b) The transmitter shall be unmodulated and its output connected to an artificial load, where the equipment is fitted with output terminals (Clause 3.1).

(c) Radiation of any spurious emissions shall be detected by the test antenna and receiver, over the frequency range 30 to 1000 MHz.

(d) At each frequency at which an emission is detected, the transmitter shall be rotated to obtain maximum response.

(e) The transmitter shall be replaced by a signal generator and dipole antenna and the effective radiated power of the emission determined by a substitution measurement.

(f) The measurements shall be repeated with the test antenna in the orthogonal polarization plane.

(g) The measurements shall be repeated with the transmitter modulated with normal test modulation (Clause 3.4).

(h) The measurements shall be repeated for any alternative integral antenna which can be supplied with the equipment.

4.5.4 Limits

Any spurious emissions from the transmitter with and without any ancillary equipment, expressed as a power into a test load or as a radiated power, in either plane of polarization, shall not exceed 50 %μW within the following frequency bands:

80 MHz - 85 MHz
87.5 MHz -118 MHz
135MHz - 136 MHz
174 MHz - 230 MHz
470 MHz - 862 MHz

The power of spurious emissions at any other frequency outside the above bands shall not exceed .25 %μW.

5. Receiver

5.1 Receiver spurious emissions

5.1.1 Definition

Spurious emissions from receivers are any emissions present at the input terminal or radiated from an integral antenna or the chassis and case of the receiver.

5.1.2 Method of measurement for equipment with antenna terminals.

(a) The methods shall be described in Clauses 4.5.2 and 4.5.3 except that the test sample shall be receiver.

5.1.3 Method of measurement for equipment incorporating integral antenna

(a) The method of measurement shall be as described in Clause 4.5.3 except that the test sample shall be the receiver.

5.1.4 Limits

Any spurious emission from a receiver, expressed either as a power into a test load or as a radiated power, shall not exceed 20 %μW on any frequency.

6. Accuracy of measurement

The tolerance for the measurement of the following parameters shall be as given below:

6.1.1	DC voltage	±3%
6.1.2	AC mains voltage	±3%
6.1.3	AC mains frequency frequency	±0.5%
6.2.1	Audio-frequency voltage, power ,etc.	±0.5 dB
6.2.2	Audio frequency	
6.2.3	Distortion and noise, etc. of audio frequency generators	1%

6.3.1	Radio frequency	± 50Hz
6.3.2	Radio-frequency voltage	± 2 dB
6.3.3	Radio frequency field strength	± 3 dB
6.3.4	Radio frequency carrier power (ERP)	± 2 dB
6.4.1	Impedance of artificial loads, combining units, cables, plugs, attenuators,etc.	± 5%
6.4.2	Source impedance of generatore and input impedance of measuting receivers	± 10 %
6.4.3	Attenuation of attenuators	± 0.5 dB
6.5.1	Temperature	± 1°C
4.5.2	Humidity	± 5%

7. Interpretation of this specification

7.1 Application of limits in tests for conformity with this specification

Tests shall be made

7.1.1 Either on a sample of appliances of the type using the statistical method of evaluation set out in 7.1.4

7.1.2 Or for simplicity's sake on one item only. The value measured must be at least 2 dB less than the limit value.

7.1.3 Subsequent tests are necessary form time to time on items taken at random from the production especially in the case of 7.1.2. In the case of any dispute which could lead to proceedings under the Wireless Telegraphy Act, such proceedings shall be considered only after tests have been carried out in accordance with 7.1.1.

71.4. Statistical assessment of compliance shall be made as follows: This test shall be performed on a sample of not less than five and not more than 12 items of the type, but if in exceptional circumstances five item are not available, the a sample of three or four shall be used. Compliance is achieved when the following relationship is met:

$x + kS_n$ is less (than or equal to) L, where

x is the arithmetical mean value of the interference levels on n items in the sample. S_n is the standard deviation of the sample, where

$$Sn^2 = 1/_{n-1} \Sigma (x-x)$$

x is the interference level of an individual item

k is the factor derived from tables of the non-central t-distribution which ensures with 80% confidence that 80% or more of the production is below the limit. Values of k as a function of n are given in the table below.

L is the limit

x, x, Sn , and L are expressed logarithmically

[dB(uV) or dB (pW)]

n	3	4	5	6	7	8	9	10	11	12
k	2.04	1.69	1.52	1.42	1.35	1.30	1.27	1.24	1.21	1.20

7.2 For the purpose of this specification, any reference to manufacturers includes importers and assemblers.

Appendix C:

TEN CODE   *Used by CBers*

10-1	Receiving poorly	10-33	EMERGENCY TRAFFIC AT THIS STATION
10-2	Receiving well		
10-3	Stop transmitting	10-34	TROUBLE AT THIS STATION HELP NEEDED
10-4	OK, Message received		
10-5	Relay message		
10-6	Busy, stand by	10-35	Confidential information
10-7	Out of service, leaving air, not working	10-36	Correct time is __
		10-37	Wrecker needed at __
10-8	In service, subject to call, working well	10-38	Ambulance needed at __
		10-39	Your message delivered
10-9	Repeat message	10-41	Please tune to channel __
10-10	Transmission completed working well	10-42	Traffic accident at __
		10-43	Traffic tie-up at __
10-11	Talking too fast	10-44	I have a message for you (or for __)
10-12	Visitors present		
10-13	Advise weather/road conditions	10-45	All units within range please report
10-16	Make pickup at __	10-46	Assist motorist
10-17	Urgent business	10-50	Break channel
10-18	Anything for us?	10-55	Intoxicated driver (DWI)
10-19	Nothing for you, return to base	10-60	What is next message number?
10-20	My location is __	10-62	Unable to copy, use phone
10-21	Call by telephone	10-63	Network directed to __
10-22	Report in person to __	10-64	Network is clear
10-23	Stand by	10-65	Awaiting your next message
10-24	Completed last assignment	10-66	Cancel message
10-25	Can you contact	10-67	All units comply
10-26	Disregard last information	10-68	Repeat message
		10-69	Message received
10-27	I am moving to channel __	10-70	Fire at __
		10-71	Proceed with transmission in sequence
10-28	Identify your station		
10-29	Time is up for contact	10-73	Speed trap at __
10-30	Does not conform to FCC rules	10-74	Negative
		10-75	You are causing interference
10-32	I will give you a radio check		
		10-77	Negative contact

10-81	Reserve hotel room for __	**10-93**	Check my frequency on this channel
10-82	Reserve room for __		
10-84	My telephone number is __	**10-94**	Please give me a long count
10-85	My address is __	**10-95**	Transmit dead carrier for 5 seconds
10-88	Advise phone number of __	**10-97**	Check test signal
10-89	Radio repairman needed at __	**10-99**	Mission completed, all units secure
10-90	I have TV interference	**10-100**	Restroom stop
10-91	Talk closer to mike	**10-200**	Police needed at __
10-92	Your transmitter is out of adjustment	**73's**	Best wishes
		88's	Love and kisses

Common Medical Terms

Arrest	A patient whose heart or respiration has stopped.
Arrhythmia	Abnormal heart rhythm.
BP	Blood Pressure.
CCU	Coronary Care Unit where serious heart patients are hospitalized.
Code Blue	Cardiac arrest.
Defibrilator	A device which shocks the heart into rhythm.
EKG	Electrocardiogram.
ER	Emergency room.
ICU	Intensive Care Unit, where critically ill patients are hospitalized.
IV	Intravenous, administering fluids intravenously.
MI	Myocardial Infarct: heart attack.
MICU	Mobile Intensive Care Unit
OB	Obstetrics: childbirth
OR	Operating room.
Sinus Rhythm	The normal rhythm of the heart.
STAT	Immediately.
Vital Signs	Blood pressure, pulse, breathing rate, temperature.

Appendix D:
SSB Codes

R-S Reports

Example: Your signal is coming in 5 by 9 here.

Readability

1 - Unreadable
2 - Barely readable
3 - Readable with difficulty
4 - Readable with little difficulty
5 - Perfectly readable

Signal Strength (S-Meter reading)

1 - Barely perceptible
2 - Very weak signal
3 - Weak signal
4 - Fair signal
5 - Fairly good signal
6 - Good signal
7 - Moderately strong signal
8 - Strong signal
9 - Extremely strong signal

International Q-Signals Used by Single Sideband Operators

QRA	Name or handle	QRV	I am ready
QRE	Estimated time of arrival	QRX	Call back later, stand by
QRG	Exact Frequency	QRZ	Who is calling me?
QRH	Frequency varies	QSA	Readability
QRL	Busy	QSB	Fading signal
QRM	Interference from other stations	QSL	Acknowledge receipt
		QSM	Repeat the last message
QRN	Natural interference static	QSO	Communications with, contact
QRO	Increase transmitter power	QSP	I will relay
		QSX	Listening on the channel
QRP	Decrease transmitter power	QSY	Change frequency
		QSZ	Send each word or sentence more than once
QRQ	Transmit faster		
QRS	Transmit more slowly	QTH	Locations
QRT	Stop transmitting	QTR	Correct time is
QRU	I have nothing for you		

Appendix E

CHANNEL JIVE (CBers Lingo)

We compiled this list of CB jargon while listening to breakers in both North America and Europe over the past ten years. While CB lingo is a kind of living language that continues to change and develop, many of the terms used way back in the 1970s are still as popular today as they were when they first were coined.

A bit 10-1 (British) - Weak or fading out
A little help - Extra power
Ace (British) - CBer with an unjustified high opinion of himself
Adios - Leaving the air
Advertising - A marked police car with lights on
Affirmative - Yes
Alligator station - "All mouth and no ears"
Ally Pally, Alexander's Palace (British) - A Favorite London DX point
    for mobiles
Anchored modulator - Base station operator
Appliance operator - A CBer who doesn't know anything about his
    radio
Aggro (British) - Aggravation
Ancient modulator - Station using Amplitude Modulation (AM)
Angle modulation - An obscure term for Frequency Modulation not to
    be confused with AM
Auntie Beep (British) - The BBC
Back door - Vehicle behind you watching what's on the motorway
Back 'em on down, back 'em on out - Ending CB conversation
Background - Noise or static on the channel
Back side, Back stroke, Bounce around, flip-flop - Return trip
Back off the hammer - Slow down
Back stroke - Return trip
Bad Scene - Crowded channels
Bagging - Police catching speeders
Bail out - Leaving the super slab at a roundabout
Band Bender - SSB operator
Barley pop - Beer
Barn - Truck garage
Base - Stationary rig
Basement - Channel 1
Bean store - Restaurant or road stop where food is served
Bear - Police
Bear bait - Someone driving fast without a radio
Bear bite - Speeding ticket
Bear cave, cage, den - Police station

Bear in the bushes - Police hiding

Bear's lair - Police station

Barefoot - Transmitting without a burner

Bear story - Police location report

Beating the bushes - Vehicle driving ahead of a group and going just enough over the speed limit (but not fast enough to get a ticket) to bring out any hidden police cars to investigate; lead vehicle watching for speed traps.

Beaver - Small, furry, large-toothed animal that lives in the water

Bells - Hours: 9 bells is nine o'clock

Bending my ears (British) - Putting me on

Bending my windows - Real good copy

Better cool it - Slow down or stop transmitting

Better half - Your wife or husband

Between the sheets - To sleep

Big brother - Police (US) Home Office, GPO (Great Britain)

Big Circle (British) - North Circular Rd. in London

Big Dummy - Truck driver term for a tractor trailer

Big Ears - Good Receiver

Big Ten Four, Four Roger for Sure, Ten Roger Four, Ten Roger D., Four Ten Roger, Roger Roger, Roger, Dodger, - Yeah

Big Wheels (British) - Lorry

Big slab (British) - Motorway

Big Smoke (British) - London

Big Twig (British) - 9 foot whip

Bird in the air - Unidentified helicopter or airplane

Bird Cage (British) - Heathrow Airport

Bit on the seat of the britches - Got a ticket

Black and White - Police car

Black and White CBer - Police with CB

Black Water - Coffee

Bleeding Over - Station spilling over onto nearby channels, usually caused by overmodulation

Bleeper breaker - Transmitting a bleep when you let off your mike, signifies end of transmission

Blinkin' Winkin - School Bus

Blood Box - Ambulance

Blowin' Smoke - Coming in loud and clear (making my rig smoke)

Blue light - Police vehicle

Boat anchor - A big old radio

Bob Tail - Semi tractor running without a trailer.

Bodacious - Loud, sounding good

Bootlegging - Using another station other than your own, illegal station

Bootleggers - Skip Talkers Club

Boots, shoes, galoshes - Kickers

Bottle popper - Beverage truck
Bottle shop (British) - Pub
Bottom of the shop - Channel 1
Break - Call a station
Break, Break; Breakity, break; Breaker, break, etc. - What you say to get on a channel
Breaker - CB user
Breaker on the side (British) - Station trying to break an ongoing conversation
Breaking up - Your signal is cutting on and off
Bring it back - Said at the end of transmission
Brought yourself on up - Put the hammer down and come this way
Brown Bottles - Beer
Brown Bottle Shop - Tavern or Pub
Bubble gum machine - Vehicle with flashing lights or revolving lights on top of the car
Bucket mouth - CBer who won't shut up
Bull jockey - Someone who shoots a lot of bull on CB
Bumper lane - Passing lane on a four-lane road
Burner - Illegal Radio Power Amplifier
Burning up my ears - Got a good signal
Bushels - Half-tons, one thousand pounds
Buzby (British) - General Post Office
Camera - Hand-held radar unit
Candles - Years
Candy Man - FCC
CB Land - The land where CB communications happen and folks on CB meet
Catch a few "z's" - Get some sleep
Chalk a block (British) - All channels filled up with breakers
Channel master - Someone who tries to monopolize or control the activities on a channel
Charlie - The FCC also Uncle Charlie
Chicken box - CB radio
Chicken choker - Jerk, wanker
Chicken coop - Truck inspection station
Chicken inspector - Weigh station inspector
Choo choo train - Semi hauling two trailers
Clean, clean and green, Clean shot - Road is clear of smokeys
Clear, off and clear - Signing off
Come back - Say it, or say it again
Come on, bring it on - Go ahead
Coming out the windows - Real good copy
Convoy - A few vehicles trucking together
Cop Shop - Police station
Copy? - Did you get that last transmission ?

Copy, copy! - Got a copy on you !

Copying the mail - Listening to folks on the channel

Cotton picker - Fellow CBer

County mountie - County sherriff

Cubs - Police

C'mon - Go ahead and transmit

Definitely, definatory - Sure will

Diesel car - Semi-tractor truck

Diesel digit - Channel 19

Dinosaur juice (British) - Petrol

Dodgy (British) - Risky

Dog - Greyhound bus

Dog Biscuits - dB, decibels

Doing it to it - Hammer down, traveling right along, not wasting any
time

Don't feed the bears - Don't get busted

Double L - Land line or telephone

Double Nickel - 55 miles an hour (approximately)

Doubled - Two stations transmitted at the same time

Doughnut (British) - Roundabout

Draggin' wagon - Wrecker

Dummy - Cop car parked as a decoy

Dusting your britches (US) or knickers (British) - Keying down on top
of another station

DX - Long distance, skip

Ears - Antennas

Ear wigging (British) - Monitoring, listening on the side to ongoing
conversation

Eat-em up stop - Restaurant or truck stop

Easy chair - Sitting in the middle of a convoy, also called a rocking
chair

Eights, Eighty-eights - Hugs and kisses, good wishes, good numbers

Eleven Meters - CB band

Eye in the sky - Airplanes checking speed

Eyeties (British) - Italian stations

Factory - Place of work, any kind of place for work

Fat load - Overweight load

Ferry lights (British) - Traffic lights

Fetch it back - Same as bring it back

Feed the bears - Pay a ticket

Fifty dollar lane - Left-most lane, or passing lane

Final - Last transmission; also, final power amplifier circuit

First person - Your name

Flag waver - Highway worker

Flappers (British) - Antennas, twigs, etc.

Flat side - Horizontal Polarization (also - Going to sleep)

Flat talking - Talking on the ground wave
Flip, flip-flop, flipper - Return trip, also U-turn
Fluff stuff - Snow
Fly in the sky - Aircraft, possibly Smokeys
Foot warmer - Linear amplifier
Forty weight - Coffee
Front door - Vehicle ahead of you, or at the head of a convoy
For fer sure - Definatory, 10-4
Full quieting - When an FM CB station is coming through with no
    background noise
Funny Candy Company - FCC Gear Jammer - Truck driver
Give a shout - Give a call
Go juice (British) - Petrol
Going breaker break - Leaving the air
Going down - Signing off the air
Going horizontal - Lying down, going to sleep; also switching to
    horizontal polarization
Going thataway - Signing off; also heading away from the home twenty
Going thisaway - Heading toward the home twenty
Golden numbers - Good numbers
Gone, we gone - Signing off, clearing the channel
Good buddy - Originally a term for fellow CBer, now often used
    derisively
Good lady - Female CBer
Good numbers and goodly numbers - Best regards and good wishes
Got a copy? - Do you hear me?
Got your ears on? - Do you hear me?
Grass - Median strip or along side of road
Green light - Clear road on up ahead
Green shield stamps (British) - money
Green stamps (US) - Money; also, issuing tickets
Green stamp road - Toll road
Ground clouds - Fog
Guarantold you - I'm telling you the truth
Guy - Fellow trucker
Haircut palace - Low clearance overpass
Handle - CB nickname
Ham - An amateur radio operator
Hammer - Acclerator peddle
Harry Rags (British) - Cigarettes
Harvey Wallbanger - Reckless driver
High channels - Channels above 40
High numbers - Same as good numbers
Hit the sheets - Going to sleep
Holding on to your mudflaps - Driving right behind you
Hole in the wall - Tunnel

Home twenty - Location of your house
Honey bear - Female police officer
Horizontal, flat side - Go to bed; also horizontally polarized antenna
How about it? - Come back; say it; we're calling you
Idiot Box - TV
In a short - Soon
In a short short - Real soon
Invitations - Police traffic citations, tickets
Is that a four? - 10-4?
Jam jar, jam butty - Same as jam sandwich
Jam sandwich (British) - Police vehicle white with red stripe through the middle
Jaw jacking - Long winded conversation
Keep it clean and don't be seen - Don't get busted
Klicks - Kilometers
Knock it down - Go down to another channel
Knock it up - Go up to another channel as in "Knock it up once".
Keep 'em between the ditches - Have a safe trip
Keep the shiny side up and the greasy side down - Have a safe trip
Kicker - Linear amplifier
Land line - Telephone
Lay-by (British) - Lorry pull-off
Linear - Linear amplifier, illegal amplifier of signal, burner
Little box - Moble linear amplifier
Little wheels (British) - Car or other four wheeled vehicle
Local yokel - Local police
Local smokel - Local or city police
Looney-channels - Channels where the ripoffs hang out
Looking thataway - Looking for a smokey report
Loose boardwalk - Bumpy road
Lucky number - A CB channel (hopefully clear)
Making the trip - You're getting out, I can hear you
Mama bear - Policewoman
Marijuana taxi - Fully outfitted police cruiser
Marker - Mile marker, milepost on the highway
May Day - International emergency distress call
May the blue light never shine on you (British) - Hope you don't get busted
Mercey sakes! - Wow!
Messers - Stations that deliberately cause interference
Modjitating - Talking
Modulation is 100% - Your signal sounds real good
Motion lotion - Gasoline, diesel, petrol
Mud - Coffee
Muppet show (British) - AM 40 channels
Nap trap - Rest area; also motel

Negatory - No
Nelly Kelly (British) - TV
Nerd - Silly CB user
Nice one - Good copy
Nickel channel - Channel 5
Noddies (British) - Motorcycle police
Non-sus twig (British) - A disguised CB antenna
Nosebag - A meal
On channel - On the air
On frequency - In calibration
On the peg - Legal speed limit
On the side - Standing by on the channel
One armed bandit - Gas pump
One eyed monster - TV set
Over your shoulder - Behind you
Over - End of transmission, your return
Patch - Town
Peanut butter in the ears - Someone who can't hear too good has this problem
Peanut whistle - Low powered station; also, station with no kicker
Pedal to the metal, hammer down - Accelerator to the floor
Peeling off (British) - Getting off the motorway
Personal - Your name
Pick a lucky number - Pick a CB channel to move to
Picture taker - Radar
Pictures - Radar
Plain wrapper - An unmarked police car
Porcupine - Mobile with lots of antennas
Portable chicken coop - Mobile weighing station
Portable parking lot - Auto carrier
Post - Marker
Pounds - Watts, notches on the "S" meter "You're putting about 9 pounds on my meter"
Pull the big switch - Turn off the CB, go of the air
Pulling cobwebs over my eyes (British) - Tricking me
Pushing big wheels - Driving a lorry
Pushing candles - How many years old
Pushing wheels - Driving a vehicle
Put an eyeball on ya - See you in person
Put up my teeth for the night - Go 10-7, sign off
Puts me off (British) - Makes me uptight
QSL Card - Postcard with handle exchanged by CBers
Radio check - Asking for a report on how your rig sounds
Ratchet jaw -Someone with a lot to say
Ratcheting - Talking
Reading the mail - Listening to the channel

Rest 'em up stop - Rest area

Rig - CB radio; also big truck or vehicle

Riot squad - Neighbors complaining about TV interference

Rock - Radio crystal

Rocking chair - That's what you are sitting in when you're in contact with mobiles ahead and behind you

Roger Bleep - A CB signaling tone device

Roger rolling skate - A four-wheeler going in and out fast between trucks

Roller skate - A small car, such as a compact or import

Rolling roadblock - Vehicle going under the speed limit and holding up traffic

Round about - Intersections on the super slab

Rubber Bander - Green CB operator, beginner on CB

Russian Woodpecker - Russian long range radar that sounds like a woodpecker and causes interference to CB

"S" unit - "S" meter reading increment

Sailboat fuel - running on an empty gas tank; also, no load in trailer

Seeing eye dog - Device which detects police radar

Seat cover - Female Passenger

Sidewinder - SSB operator

Shake the trees and rake the leaves - Lead vehicle watch ahead and rear vehicle watch behind, in a group of CB vehicles in CB contact

Shoes - Burner

Show-off lane (US only) - Left hand lane

Skating rink - Slippery road conditions

Skip land - Any place further away than 60 miles

Skip talker - A CBer who talks long distances

Slider - VFO, a device used to make CB's tune all across the channels, in between them, and then some

Smoke it on - Go ahead, over, bring it on

Smokey, smokey the bear - Police

Smokey report - Location of Smokey the bear

Smokey Town (British) - London

Sounding choice - Got a good sounding signal

Spaghetti Junction (British) - Birmingham, England

Sparks - Radio technicians

Squawk box - CB radio

Squeakee, squeaker (British) - Rip off station, usually talks in a high squeaky voice

Square wheels - A stopped vehicle

Suicide sleeper - Truck with sleeper over cab

Super skate - Sportscar

Station on the side - CBer waiting to join on-going conversation on the channel

Stateside skip - Skip from the USA

Stinger - Top part of a CB antenna usually a stainless steel whip

Suicide jockey - Truck driver carrying hazardous materials
Super slab - Interstate (US) or Motorway (Great Britain)
Sweet thing - Lady on the channel
Taking pictures - Police using radar
Ten-ten till we do it again (British) - Sign off
That's a fox (British) - 10-4
Thermos bottle - Tanker truck
Top of the shop - Channel 40
Tower Town (British) - Blackspool
Treading wheels - Same as pushing wheels
Three's, 3's, 73's - Good luck, best wishes
Tijiuana taxi - State trooper car with lights, sirens, etc.
Train station - Court with high guilty rate
Trip around the horn (British) - Scanning through the channels
Truck 'em easy - Take it easy driving
TVI - Television interference
Twig (British) - Antenna
Twins - Dual antennas
Twister - Highway interchange
Two wheeler - Motorcycle or bicycle
Vertical - Vertical ground plane antenna
Vertical side - Vertical polarization
Walking all over you - Another louder station is covering up your signal
Walking tall - Good sounding signal
Walking the dog - Talking over a long distance
Wall paper - QSL cards, exchanged by CBers, that have their call sign, handle and location printed on them
Wall to wall and tree top tall - Loud and clear signal
Wall to wall bears - Lots of smokeys
Wall to wall spaghetti (British) - Overcrowded with Italian skip
Wally - Crazy operator
Watering hole - Pub
We up, we down, we gone bye bye! - Sign off
Weight watcher - Mobile truck weighing station
What am I putting on you? - How well can you hear me? What does your "S" meter read?
What about ya? - Are you there?
Willy Weaver - Drunken driver
Windup - A put on
Wrapper - Vehicle
X-Band - Radar frequency Smokeys use
X-Ray machine - Radar
XYL - Wife
YL - Young lady
Z's - Sleep
Zoo - Police headquarters

Appendix F:

British and American CB Channel Frequencies

Ch.	British	American	Ch.	British	American
1	27.60125	26.965	21	27.80125	27.215
2	27.61125	26.975	22	27.81125	27.225
3	27.62125	26.985	23	27.82125	27.255
RC*		26.995	24	27.83125	27.235
4	27.63125	27.005	25	27.84125	27.245
5	27.64125	27.015			
6	27.65125	27.025	26	27.85125	27.265
7	27.66125	27.035	27	27.86125	27.275
RC*		27.045			
8	27.67125	27.055	28	27.87125	27.285
9	27.68125	27.065	29	27.88125	27.295
10	27.69125	27.075	30	27.89125	27.305
11	27.70125	27.085	31	27.90125	27.315
RC*		27.095			
12	27.71125	27.105	32	27.91125	27.325
13	27.73125	27.115	33	27.92125	27.335
14	27.74125	27.125	34	27.93125	27.345
15	27.75125	27.135	35	27.94125	27.355
RC*		27.145			
16	27.76125	27.155	36	27.95125	27.365
17	27.76125	27.165	37	27.96125	27.375
18	27.77125	27.175	38	27.97125	27.385
19	27.78125	27.185	39	27.98125	27.395
RC*		27.195			
20	27.79125	27.205	40	27.99125	27.405

*RC = Radio Control Channel; not legally available in the US for voice communications.

British 934 MegaHertz CB Band

Channels   Channels

1	934.025
2	934.075
3	934.125
4	934.175
5	934.225
6	934.275
7	934.325
8	934.375
9	934.425
10	934.475

11	934.525
12	934.575
13	934.625
14	934.675
15	934.725
16	934.775
17	934.825
18	934.875
19	934.925
20	934.975

Appendix G:

Time and Metric Conversions

1 millimeter (mm) =	.039 inches
1 centimeter (cm) =	.39 inches
1 meter (m) =	39.40 inches, 3.28 feet
1 kilometer (km) =	.62 miles
1 inch (in.) =	2.54 cm
1 foot (ft.) =	30.48 cm
1 yard (yd.) =	.914 meter
1 mile =	1.6 km

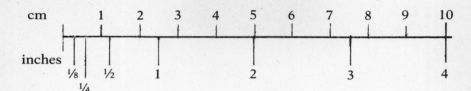

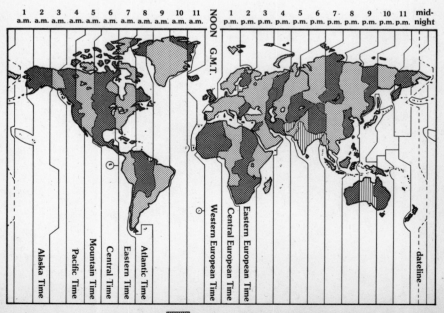

COUNTRIES WITH TIME OTHER THAN THEIR ZONE.

Index

About the Authors

Mark Long (Stringbean) was first introduced to the fascinating world of electronic communications in 1965, when his father installed a mobile CB rig in the family car. A licensed radio amateur (WA4LXC), shipboard radio operator and radar technician, Mr Long has held HAM radio licenses in five countries, coordinated radio communications for major disaster/relief efforts, and served as radio officer aboard the Greenpeace flagship "Rainbow Warrior." Since 1984, Mark has been the president of MLE Inc., a Florida-based corporation which specializes in technical publishing for telecommunications professionals. He is the author of the **Down to Earth Guide to Satellite TV**, the **World Satellite Almanac** and the **Ku-Band Satellite Handbook,** and the co-author of the **World of Satellite Television.**

Albert Houston (White Lightning). A CB and amateur radio enthusiast (KW4A) since 1967, Albert enjoys High Frequency DXing, making antennas, and mobiling. As a radio frequency engineer based in California's Silicon Valley, Mr. Houston has been on the leading edge of the electronics revolution, developing advanced satellite receivers, satellite telephones, pocket pagers and various specialized two-way radio services.

Jeffrey Keating (Minnesota Mumbler). Jeffrey Keating is an amateur radio operator (WB4KDH) who is particularly fascinated by recent developments in the field of slow-scan television, electronic mail-box satellites, and packet radio. Jeffrey has been an FM broadcast station manager, a radio net control operator for major relief efforts in Central America, and a pioneer member of the U.S. satellite TV industry. A concerned environmentalist and humanitarian, Jeffrey has also assisted groups like Greenpeace and the PLENTY international relief and development organization. In recent years, Jeffrey has worked as a satellite consultant and product development manager for a Miami-based export company. He is also the author of numerous magazine articles and publications, including the best-selling **World of Satellite Television.**

It's been a wild and crazy spin through CB Land. If you ever hear the Big Dummy on the channel, give out a shout, and we'll modulate a while. Until then, we're putting the Golden Numbers on you and we're on the side.